Contents

Marie Stopes, Eugenics and The English Birth Control Movement

Proceedings of a Conference organised by the Galton Institute, London, 1996

Edited by

Robert A Peel

PUBLISHED BY THE GALTON INSTITUTE, LONDON

British Library Cataloguing in Publication Data

Galton Institute. Conference (1997: London, England)

Marie Stopes, eugenics and the English birth control movement: proceedings of a conference organised by the Galton Institute, London, 1996

1. Stopes, Marie - Congresses 2. Eugenics - Congresses
3. Birth Control - England - Congresses 4. Science - Social aspects - England - Congresses

I. Title II. Peel, Robert A.

363.9'2

ISBN 0950406627

First published 1997 by The Galton Institute, 19 Northfields Prospect, Northfields, London SW18 1PE

Printed and bound in Great Britain by The Chameleon Press, 5-25 Burr Road, Wandsworth, London, SW18 4SG

Notes on the Contributors

Dr Deborah A Cohen, James Bryant Conant Fellow, Minda de Gunzburg Centre for European Studies, Harvard University USA

Dr Lesley A Hall, Senior Assistant Archivist, Contemporary Medical Archives Centre, Wellcome Institute for the History of Medicine, London

Patricia Hindmarsh, Director of External Affairs, Marie Stopes International, London

Dr John Peel, Treasurer, The Galton Institute, London

Robert A Peel, President, The Galton Institute, London

June Rose, Freelance writer and biographer of Marie Stopes

Professor Richard A Soloway, Eugen Merzbacher Chair, Department of History, The University of North Carolina at Chapel Hill, North Carolina, USA

Dr John Timson, Vice-President, The Galton Institute, London

Editor's Preface

Robert A Peel

In 1921 Marie Stopes established the first birth control clinic in the world. To mark the seventy-fifth anniversary of that event the Galton Institute organised a conference, held on 26 September 1996, at the Wellcome Institute for the History of Medicine. This book contains the papers given at that conference together with an introduction by the conference organiser.

It is appropriate that the Galton Institute should sponsor this conference and its resulting publication. Marie Stopes was a life-long Fellow of the Eugenics Society (as the Institute then was) and a great friend of Dr C P Blacker, its General Secretary from 1931 to 1952 and its Honorary Secretary from 1952 to 1961. A result of that association was that, on her death in 1958, she bequeathed her London clinic to the Eugenics Society with an expressed wish that it should be operated by the Society as an independent clinic. The Society assumed formal control of the clinic in 1960 and for the next sixteen years was directly responsible for its operation. This was a period of significant change in birth control provision and contraceptive technology and the Marie Stopes Clinic was at the forefront of many innovatory procedures and activities that have been of permanent significance.

The detailed history of those innovations has still to be written. They include special clinic sessions providing contraceptive advice to the young and unmarried from which developed the Brook Advisory Centres, now an independent organisation with 27 clinics nation-wide providing advice to 53,000 girls each year. They include, too, modern domiciliary birth control schemes (which, we learn from this book, were pioneered by Marie Stopes herself in the 1920s); out-patient vasectomy and out--patient early termination of pregnancy; the training of overseas doctors and nurses and innovative schemes of co-operation with local health authorities. A former President of the Institute, Peter Diggory (who was consultant to the clinic during much of this period) has described the Institute's involvement as having "radically transformed the English birth control clinic from the basic cap-fitting establishment which had prevailed for thirty years into a multi-functional organisation later copied by other voluntary and public bodies. The groundwork laid down in the improved birth control clinics has now expanded to be a fundamental part of the training of all doctors."

In 1976, when the provisions of the 1967 Family Planning Act had been fully implemented by local health authorities to provide free contraception as a part of the National Health Service, the Eugenics Society saw no further need for the provision of its traditional services and relinquished management of the clinic to an international organisation which, as the Marie Stopes International, has successfully continued the pioneering work of the clinic. It is now the largest private sector provider of family planning services in Britain and one of the most highly regarded non governmental organisations operating overseas. The clinic which Marie Stopes founded seventy-five years ago thus continues as a permanent memorial to her endeavours, to the ideas she held in common with the Galton Institute and to the success of the Institute in ensuring its survival during a critical transition period.

That this conference took place at the Wellcome Institute for the History of Medicine was also appropriate. The archives both of the Eugenics Society and of the Marie Stopes Memorial

Clinic are held at the Wellcome Institute where they are amongst the most frequently used of its many collections. Five of the papers given at this conference were based on research carried out at the Wellcome and are a testimony to the valuable facilities which it provides for the international academic community.

The Galton Institute is grateful to those who gave papers at the conference. It is convinced that they will be seen as a fitting tribute to one of its most famous members. We do not believe this book will represent the last word on Marie Stopes and her achievements; we hope that it will bring to a wide general readership a balanced and objective insight into a number of important aspects of her life and activities and that the quality of its scholarship will ensure that it is not overlooked by future researchers.

Introduction

John Peel

In planning the conference on which this book is based, the objects of the Institute's Council were to examine a number of the lesser known aspects of the life and achievements of Marie Stopes, to demonstrate the way in which the Marie Stopes and Eugenics Society archives are being productively researched and to stress those features of Marie Stopes' work which impinge on the traditional concerns of the Galton Institute.

There are five published biographies of Marie Stopes[12345] in all of which her early life and upbringing and her original career as a research scientist receive less attention than the turbulent events of her later years. In the next chapter of this book, June Rose, author of the most recent biography of Marie Stopes, re-explores this relatively neglected earlier period of her life and, adopting an appropriately Darwinian title reaches a predictably Galtonian conclusion. By inheritance and upbringing Marie Stopes was uniquely fitted both for her immediate career as a scientist and her subsequent "mission", as she came to see it, of applying her scientific expertise to human betterment.

The idea that science could be put to such a social purpose was ubiquitous in late Victorian and Edwardian England; science, having been seen as a challenge to religion in the 1860s and 1870s had now acquired such prestige as to become a substitute for it. The British Association for the Advancement of Science, though founded in 1831, reached its apogee in this period and, with its week-long annual meetings held successively in different major towns and cities in Britain, together with its camp followers, became the evangelical

1

church of science. It is no surprise to learn from June Rose, that Marie Stopes was a "child of the British Association".

Whereas, however, most of its disciples had only the most general idea of how science could be utilised for the purpose of human progress, Marie Stopes (like her contemporaries H G Wells and the youthful Harold Laski) had no doubt as to the appropriate vehicle. This was eugenics, the most enduring science-based social creed: a theory and a movement to which she maintained her commitment throughout her life.

First, she had to qualify herself as a scientist. Her father belonged to, and was himself an example of, the last generation of men who, without formal scientific training, and often pursuing non-scientific full-time careers, were able to make significant additions to scientific knowledge on the basis of curiosity, enthusiasm and diligence. His daughter faced the challenge of a more rigorous and daunting apprenticeship: undergraduate followed by post-graduate study. Throughout all this she, of course, excelled: a three-year degree obtained in two years, the first woman PhD at Munich, the youngest Doctor of Science in England and the first woman to receive a Royal Society research award. Yet, as she was surely aware, all this fell short of the ultimate in academic attainment. She had two doctorates but neither was in medicine, as she was frequently to be reminded by the medical press. And her *alma mater* was the University of London, officially - if perversely - classified as a provincial university. The ancient universities, then as now regarded as the twin peaks in the landscape of English academe, were forbidden to her as a woman. Although women had been allowed to attend lectures in Oxford since 1878 and to sit examinations since 1894 they were not permitted to receive degrees until 1920.[6] By that date Marie Stopes had quit academic life - but with a list of publications[7] which would put to shame most occupants of chairs in today's over-expanded university system.

Nevertheless, the scientifically trained mind which she had acquired during this meteoric passage through the academic world was evident in all her subsequent undertakings.

The thoroughness of her researches in the Reading Room of the British Museum preparatory to the writing of *Married Love*, the diligence with which she assembled the widely scattered data for her more scientific works, notably *Contraception*, and the meticulous attention to detail and record which characterised the operation of her clinics - in all of these the skills of the trained scientist were apparent. They were apparent, above all, in the analytical approach she brought to the subject of birth control at a time when her contemporaries regarded the problem in more simplistic terms.

It was Marie Stopes' involvement with the Eugenics Society and the Malthusian League (through which she had met her second husband H V Roe) which inspired her interest in and subsequent commitment to birth control. For these organisations, concerned respectively with the problem of differential fertility and over-population, the uncritical dissemination of birth control was seen as a sufficient solution. Upper- and middle-class couples had the knowledge which enabled them to control their fertility; the task was to make that knowledge more generally available. Norman Himes and other subsequent historians of the birth control movement described its aims and functions as "the democratisation of contraceptive knowledge".

To the author of *Married Love* the issue was more complex. In that book Marie Stopes had proposed "that woman like man has . . . a reciprocal need for enjoyment and benefit from union in marriage distinct from the exercise of maternal functions."

But, though she recognised that birth control had an important role in sexual relations - if for no other reason than that fear of pregnancy inhibited the frequency, spontaneity and enjoyment of those relations - she saw, too, that birth control was also an impediment to the transformation of the act of sex into that life-enhancing experience enjoined by *Married Love*.

This was Marie Stopes' great revolutionary insight. It was an insight which we now know, but which she could not have known, she shared with Freud himself. Peter Gay, Freud's most recent biographer, informs us: "We know that in the early 1890s . . . he deplored the untoward psychological consequences of contraception . . . depending on the methods employed either the man or woman is probably doomed to end up a victim of hysteria or of an anxiety neurosis." Gay then quotes Janet Malcolm: "If Freud had continued his own efforts in this direction he would have become the inventor of a better condom, not the founder of psychoanalysis."[8]

If this is really what Janet Malcolm thinks we can only be grateful that Freud left the task to Marie Stopes who realised that the condom, and every other form of contraception then in use were, by their very nature, crude impediments to any from of love making, most of all to the prolonged and hyper-sensitive techniques enjoined by *Married Love*. Instead, Marie Stopes adopted, perfected and promoted a device then little-known in England: the high-domed cervical cap. Unique amongst methods of contraception then available, this device was effective, it placed the responsibility for contraception firmly with the woman, it was non-intrusive and above all its use could be initiated at a point remote in time from the act of intercourse thus obviating the need for any interruption of the progress of that event. Indeed, with one exception (its manifest association with sex) this form of contraception then fulfilled all those requirements which were later claimed for the

"ideal contraceptive":   the Pill.   Marie Stopes was frequently
criticised for suggesting that the cap "could be fitted at any
convenient time, preferably when dressing in the evening" - a
statement which, like Mr Mervyn Griffith-Jones' question to the
jury in the Lady Chatterley trial ("Would you allow your
servants to read this book?"), has been regarded as evidence of
her social insensitivity.   It was nothing of the sort;   she was
merely stressing one of the more important attributes of her
recommended method.   Her subsequent claim that the cap
could be left in place "for days or even weeks on end" was
probably more seriously open to clinical objection.

Marie Stopes' obsession with the alleged superiority of her
cervical cap, her extravagant claims for its efficacy and her
resultant quarrels with her rivals in the family planning
movement over their promotion of alternative methods can
only be understood in the context of the unique role she
accorded it in her theory of the sexual relationship.   This theory
was both psychological and physiological.   The secretions of
sexual intercourse had, in order to be effective, to be absorbed
through the vaginal wall.   This, the cervical cap allowed.   The
alternative, the vaginal diaphragm favoured by the "opposition"
(the clinics of the SPBCC, later the Family Planning
Association), lying diagonally across the vaginal canal thus
occluding both the cervix and the upper part of the vagina[9]
inhibited this vital absorption.

Birth control was thus intrinsic to Marie Stopes' general
theory of sexual relations and consequently she had a greater
need to prove the superiority of her chosen method than the
pragmatists of the rival clinics who were concerned only with
acceptability and efficacy.   And though, as Richard Soloway
points out in Chapter 3, her method of calculating her success
rates was statistically bizarre, it must be remembered that the
standardised procedure for contraceptive use-effectiveness

calculations was not proposed until 1932[10] and it was not until 1937 that the concept of controlled trials was taken seriously by the medical profession[11]. Moreover, the evaluation of contraceptives in the 1920s was less a matter of science than of propaganda and Marie Stopes' opponents in the birth control movement were equally guilty of publishing self-serving results. Thus Marie Stopes claimed[12] a 99.4 per cent success rate for her cervical cap but imputed an 85.5 per cent failure rate to the diaphragm used by the SPBCC. In response, Dr Norman Haire, medical officer of the Walworth SPBCC clinic claimed that the diaphragm was far superior to the Stopes cap which, he alleged, had failed in 88 per cent of those cases which he had seen[13].

What both Marie Stopes and Norman Haire were in complete agreement on was the almost total unreliability of every method of birth control other than those recommended by their respective clinics.   Patients at their clinics were questioned about previous methods used and from this data, comprising 1,284 Stopes cases and 1,800 SPBCC patients the following failure rates were published:

Percentage of failures reported by:

Pre-clinic method	Stopes	Haire
Condom	75.3	51.1
Douche	95.1	73.5
Caps	—	87.5
Diaphragms	85.5	—
Quinine suppositories	98.1	70.8
Withdrawal	81.8	69.5
Safe period	100.0	100.0

Had there been available a totally reliable method of contraception which fulfilled the demands of her theories of sexual interaction it is likely that Marie Stopes would have left birth control to others and concentrated on her career as a sex counsellor and investigator. Her friends had indeed urged her to do so. "I think", wrote George Bernard Shaw, "that you should insist on the separation in the public mind of your incidental work as a scientific critic of contraception with your main profession as a teacher of matrimonial technique". In fact, her achievements in the non-birth-control field of sexual behaviour were in any case considerable. She was the first professional sex counsellor and her writings on sexual behaviour and function anticipated both Kinsey and Masters and Johnson. Her work moreover had greater validity than most subsequent investigations being based on empirical data of unequalled volume and quality.

Most sociological surveys, both in Britain and America, are based on interviews or questionnaires representing the responses of a hundred or two individuals[14]. Alfred Kinsey's classic study was unusual in being based on 5,000 respondents but these were largely self-selected and included a high proportion of students, teachers and prison inmates. Marie Stopes accumulated a data base comprising tens of thousands of letters from men and women seeking her advice, thousands of case-records of clinic patients and many thousands of other documents relevant to the running of her clinic. Her correspondents' letters provided not only a more numerous sample than has ever been available to a single researcher before or since; they were also more valuable in that they represented the unprompted testimony of writers unconstrained by the limitations of the pre-coded questionnaire. She made excellent use of these in her own writings but abstracted only a fraction of their abundant research potential which has been available to later scholars as a unique source for further historical and sociological investigation. Lesley Hall has demonstrated, not only in her paper in this volume, but also in her previous full length study, *Hidden Anxieties*, how valuable a primary source these letters remain. That earlier work was based on letters to Marie Stopes written by men, who formed forty per cent of her correspondents, and it reconstructs the sexual sociology of five decades from the frankly expressed ideas and beliefs revealed in those letters.[15]

Deborah Cohen has used a further class of documents preserved by Marie Stopes for a grateful posterity in analysing the work of her Mother's Clinics. These were the weekly reports of the clinic nursing staff which provide convincing contemporary testimony to the spirit which pervaded the work of those clinics. The friendly and sympathetic atmosphere which Marie Stopes took so much trouble to create was clearly important to, and appreciated by, her patients; the dividend was that those patients were thereby induced to co-operate in the completion of the very detailed case-sheets which she had devised. From these Marie Stopes was able to publish unique and valuable data on maternal morbidity, perinatal mortality and the prevalence of induced abortion not available from hospital records. The preservation of these thousands of clinical case records will provide yet another opportunity for further research when they become publicly available in 2008 and 2026.

A feature of the conference was the showing of the film "Marie Stopes: Secret Life" produced by Soul Purpose Productions and nationally broadcast on Channel Four TV in December 1995. In his introduction to the showing of the film, published here, John Timson makes a number of observations about the problems of popular portrayal of serious historical figures. The most general of these, the apparent need to ridicule, is not unique to the film; it has also characterised her biographies, the personal recollections of her contemporaries and almost every other commentary on her life and work. In all of these her personal idiosyncrasies have been used not merely to diminish her stature as a public figure but, in effect, to devalue her many achievements.

Iconoclasm has, of course, a comforting social function. It enables us to come to terms with our own mediocrity. Einstein, Freud and even Newton have suffered posthumously at the hands of their recent biographers. But, as applied to women, iconoclasm seems to take on an especial virulence. They are accused of arrogance, humourlessness and even masculinity. The weakness of such portrayals, as Laurie Taylor pointed out some years ago in an insightful and sympathetic study of Marie Stopes[16], is that they are a hackneyed and stereotypical response to successful women everywhere. They constitute "standard descriptions" of feminine militants which have been taken down and dusted off to provide ready-made characterisations of historically important women from Boadicea to Margaret Thatcher.

> "She moved under the stress of an impetus which finds no place in the popular imagination. She was a rock in an angry ocean. There was humour in her face; but the curious watcher might wonder whether it was humour of a very pleasant kind. Her advice flowed unceasingly in all directions. 'I have a passionel nature which requires satisfaction' she noted. She was not to be put aside by doctors; they were talking nonsense. 'We are ducks', said her mother with tears in her eyes, 'who have hatched a wild swan.' But the poor lady was wrong; it was not a swan they had hatched; it was an eagle."

The above quotation is not from one of the biographies of Marie Stopes although equivalent, if less elegantly expressed, comments could be found in all of them. It is in fact a composite quote compiled *seriatim* from Lytton Strachey's life of Florence Nightingale published in 1918[17]. Yet it is not a summary of what Strachey thought of his subject. His comments are gracefully woven into his narrative in such a way as to subtly enhance, rather than diminish Florence Nightingale and her achievements. Strachey knew the pitfalls of biography ("It is perhaps as difficult to write a good life as to live one") and he realised that his Victorian paragons were multi-faceted personalities; General Gordon's heroism is more, not less, admirable because it represented the triumph of the Bible over the brandy bottle.

Marie Stopes was also a complex personality with her fair share of human foibles. But to assemble these together and present them with all the spurious scientific authority of a psychological profile, as so many commentators have done, is not especially enlightening. Every incident in her life which betrays a defect of character can be matched by others which reveal contradictory traits. Thus, although she certainly behaved ungenerously towards members of her family she gave considerable financial help to the ailing and indigent Lord Alfred Douglas and worked hard to obtain for him a state pension. And though some of her public pronouncements about the undeserving poor were harsh, in practice and in private she showed great compassion.

This book is about Marie Stopes and birth control; it is also about eugenics. And though her life-time association with the movement was, as Richard Soloway describes, fraught with disagreements, it is a measure of the esteem in which she was held that the Eugenics Society went to considerable trouble after her death in 1958 to ensure that despite the many obstacles, her wishes regarding the future of her clinic were fulfilled. Indeed, the readiness of those with whom she disagreed to respond with good humour and even affection is a noteworthy feature of her life. Like many others, including Winston Churchill, she disliked the way Giles drew his cartoon figures; in 1949 she wrote to the *Daily Express* to say that she would not take the paper again "so long as you poison it with Giles' productions"[18]. Giles' response was published alongside his "Fan Mail from Dr Marie Stopes" in the form of another cartoon[19].

REPLY

Very well, Marie, if you're not going to take the *Express* any more because of my cartoons, I'm not going to read any more of your little books.

Simon Jenkins, recently reviewing the final volume, 1900-1990, of the *Penguin History of Britain*, points out that "Marie Stopes and William Beveridge receive as much credit for advancing human happiness as Churchill and Attlee"[20]. Since Beveridge, like Marie Stopes, was a life-long supporter of the

Eugenics Society this is a judgement which members of the Galton Institute are hardly likely to dispute.

References:

[1] Aylmer Maude, *The Authorised Life of Marie C. Stopes,* Williams and Norgate, London, 1924.

[2] Aylmer Maude, *Marie Stopes, Her Work and Play,* Putnam , London, 1933.

[3] Keith Briant, *Marie Stopes, a Biography*, Hogarth Press, London, 1962.

[4] Ruth Hall, *Marie Stopes, a Biography*, Andre Deutsch, London, 1977.

[5] June Rose, *Marie Stopes and the Sexual Revolution*, Faber and Faber, London, 1992.

[6] V H H Green, *A History of Oxford University*, B T Batsford, London, 1974. The University of Cambridge did not award degrees to women until 1947.

[7] Peter Eaton and Marilyn Warnick, *Marie Stopes; A Checklist of her Writings*, Croom Helm, London, 1977.

[8] Peter Gay, *Freud: A Life for Our Time*, Norton, London, 1988.

[9] John Peel and Malcolm Potts, *Textbook of Contraceptive Practice.* Cambridge University Press, 1969.

[10] This was "Pearl's Formula", still the accepted method of measuring contraceptive failure rates and first published: Raymond Pearl, *Human Biology 4*, 1932.

[11] See: Galton Institute *Newsletter*, No. 1, May 1991, pp. 5-6

[12] Marie Stopes, *The First Five Thousand*, London, 1925

[13] N Haire, *Practitioner III*, 1923.

[14] John Peel and Gordon Skipworth, "Sample Size: An Innovatory Procedure in Survey Analysis", *Sociology* 4,3 1970.

[15] Lesley A Hall, *Hidden Anxieties: Male Sexuality, 1900-1950*, London, Polity Press, 1991.

[16] Laurie Taylor, "The Unfinished Sexual Revolution", *Journal of Biosocial Science*, (1971), Vol 3, 473-492.

[17] Lytton Strachey, *Eminent Victorians*, London: Chatto and Windus, 1918.

[18] Peter Tory, *Giles: A Life in Cartoons*, Headline: London, 1992

[19] Reproduced courtesy of Express Newspapers

[20] *Sunday Times*, 27 October 1996.

The Evolution of Marie Stopes

June Rose

Most of the conference papers which make up subsequent chapters in this book will concentrate principally on Marie Stopes' great work as a pioneer of birth control. But she had had an outstanding career as a scientist before she became known to the world as a "sexpert". She had that curious quality which we call charisma; in her case intellectual brilliance and emotional intensity, a woman who brought sparks and fire to every subject she broached. Had she lived today, she would still be regarded as extreme and shocking and, I suspect, she would be in constant demand to appear on television and the radio.

As a human being she was extremely complex and contradictory. She was both a passionate scientist and an analytical lover, a woman who could merge what E M Forster called "the prose and the passion" in order to dissect the emotional and sexual needs of both men and women. When it came to her own, personal life she was inconsistent and incredibly naive, capable of extraordinary kindness and benevolence yet sometimes ruthless and cruel. In this chapter I want very briefly to try to place Marie Stopes' work in the context of her time and then to talk about the evolution of one of the most remarkable women of our century.

By the close of the first World War, Marie Stopes was thirty-eight and, in a sense, her life was just beginning. After one unsuccessful marriage she had at last found a satisfactory mate, Humphrey Roe, a handsome pilot in the Royal Flying Corps, who had helped to pay for the printing of the book she had planned for years, '*Married Love*'. Above all the book, subtitled

13

"a New Contribution to the Solution of Sex Difficulties" was instantly popular - and apparently helpful.

After the elation of the Armistice, a mood of anti-climax combined with release permeated the country. By the 1920s, the troops who returned home were disappointed and disillusioned. They had discovered that their country was not yet a land fit for heroes; many of them could not even find a job. The civilian population too was dismayed to find that a huge number of returning heroes were infected with venereal disease (one in five was the official estimate). As for the heroines, a grateful nation had, it is true, given the vote to women over 30 and passed a Sex Disqualification Removal Act in recognition of women's war service. But in practice women still suffered from discrimination in almost every sphere of life: education; the law; finance; work, the list was endless. Due to the slaughter of troops on the battle field, tens of thousands of "surplus women" in the country were regarded with deep suspicion. Despite their bright hopes, women discovered that the chance to play their full part in the national life in the post-war world remained a mirage.

The emergence of Marie Stopes, then, with her confidence and her campaigning speeches, her birth control clinic and her books offered a new promise to women.

Vera Brittain, the writer, one of the most thoughtful of the young intellectuals of her day attended meetings of Marie's "Society for Constructive Birth Control" in 1922 and was immensely impressed by the "young face, soft voice and the youthful garments of the confident and dauntless founder." Marie's crusade, according to Vera Brittain, was "one of the soundest hopes for the liberation of women from traditional restrictions and burdens."[1]

But Marie had also made enemies. By publishing affordable works on contraception and venereal disease, and by writing articles for the popular press on sex and birth control she had broken the taboos against giving advice to the poor and to the young. The Churches, particularly the Roman Catholics, were, of course, incensed. The medical profession too, ignorant of contraception for the most part, opposed her work and many feared that she had gone too far: "Her books are read extensively and secretly in girls' schools and by boys in the same spirit that indecent literature in general is enjoyed. In fact, in one sense, they can be considered as practical books of prostitution."[2] That comment was made in an article written for a professional journal, *Guy's Hospital Gazette*, in 1924 by Dr C P Blacker, a member of the Eugenics Society.

The year before that article was published, 1923, Marie had had a play, "Our Ostriches" staged at the Royal Court Theatre and a film "Maisie's Marriage" shown at cinemas throughout the country. Both works were thinly disguised tracts on birth control. Due to a much publicised libel suit her name figured prominently in the headlines and she was so well known that she was recognised in the streets of London, a sure sign of public notice in the days before television. In playgrounds all over the country, schoolgirls chanted with glee:

"Jeanie, Jeanie full of hopes
Read a book by Marie Stopes
But to judge from her condition,
She must have read the wrong edition!"

She was in her early forties at the time, born in the Victorian era, yet modern woman personified.

The question that posed itself when I began to write her biography was: "Where had she come from? And how could a woman who was, admittedly a Doctor of Science but had no

medical qualifications, have acquired the information and
gained the confidence to galvanise public opinion and head
such a dangerous campaign?" My researches led me to the
womb of the British Museum, the old Reading Room. Under
Stopes, I found dozens of entries of Marie's work, not only her
major sociological books, but volumes of poetry, plays, novels,
a children's fairy story as well as scientific publications. More
surprisingly, I discovered that both of her parents had work
published, her mother's output exceeding her father's.

Charlotte Carmichael Stopes was born in Edinburgh in 1841,
soon after Queen Victoria came to the throne. At a time when
women were ineligible for university entrance, Charlotte, who
was clever and persistent, had battled to acquire a higher
education for herself. At the age of twenty-six she finally
discovered extra-mural courses run for women by sympathetic
professors and she gained the equivalent of a degree in both
arts and sciences. Charlotte went on to become a serious
Shakespearean scholar writing erudite articles on the life and
times of the bard. More pertinently to my purpose, she became
a feminist long before the term was coined, a staunch advocate
of the Women's Cause, writing and lecturing in forthright tones
on the injustices suffered by women. Let me give you an
example: "The lawyers of the nineteenth century have decided
that the word 'man' always includes 'woman' where there is a
penalty to be incurred but never includes woman where there
is a privilege to be conferred".[3]

Charlotte had a sharp, incisive mind and in the early
struggles of the Suffragists before the first World War, she was
more militant than her daughter. In her photographs Charlotte
has the appearance of a martinet. There she stands erect, a
stern and uncompromising Victorian lady, tightly laced and
corseted, and dressed in a crinoline with a flounced skirt and
bustle. Charlotte came late to marriage and to motherhood and

never really settled to her role. She was thirty-eight to her husband, Henry Stopes', twenty-seven. By the time her two daughters, Marie born in 1880 and Winnie four years later, were growing into girlhood Charlotte had abandoned the crinoline to wear flowing and loose fitting garments. She had joined the Rational Dress Society, one of the many worthy causes she espoused, and she even delivered a paper to the British Association for the Advancement of Science on the subject, informing her audience that the fashion for tight lacing was considered passé by London couturiers. The two Stopes girls stood out from their contemporaries by wearing loose knitted garments instead of dressing like miniature Victorian ladies. Marie disliked being made to look different at the time but later retained her mother's distaste for corsets and for brassieres when they came in. Long before the feminists in this century burned their bras, the women in the Stopes family had refused to wear them.

From the beginning Charlotte had intended her eldest daughter to be an outstanding woman and the first diary entry on Marie's intellectual development was for November 1880 when the infant was a month old: "the baby has shewn considerable enjoyment in life, rarely objecting to its manifestations. She loves to toast her feet at the fire, to be bathed, to be chucked under the chin, to be sung to . . ."

Nor did Charlotte neglect her baby's physical education. At the age of ten months, on holiday in the Isle of Wight, Marie was dipped into the cold sea every day, even if the winds were bitter and the waves strong.

Herself a former governess, Charlotte gave Marie her first lessons when she was five years old. The little girl tottered into her mother's room each morning, carrying a pile of books. Her curriculum included Geography and History, the roots of English language, grammar and composition as well as the rudiments of Latin and Greek. Not surprisingly the little girl did not always succeed in pleasing her mother. Soon however, Charlotte's own intellectual pursuits kept her away from home and if she was forced to stay away for a night or two, Marie, at the age of eight, was expected to supervise the maid, keep an eye on her younger sister and make sure that her father was properly fed.

Mother and daughter clashed frequently, for Charlotte, though pious and devoted, was rather chilly and disapproving both to her husband and to her daughters. Over a hundred years ago Charlotte was struggling to combine work outside the home with family life with the result that she was in a permanent muddle. Nevertheless Charlotte had set her daughter a formidable example of respect for the intellect, disregard for convention and of the need to place work in the world above home comforts.

Henry Stopes looked up to his wife with something approaching awe. He admired her, but had hoped for more passion and more affection in his marriage. She had looked for more piety in Henry and found constraints of domesticity difficult. Both parents grumbled about each other in letters to their elder daughter and she often had to act as go-between. Marie turned to her father for warmth and affection and he and his daughter drew support from each other.

Marie often used to say that she was a child of the British Association for the Advancement of Science. That was where her parents first met; all three of them were interested in the new ideas current at the turn of the century and Marie, like her parents, became an active member when she grew up.

Her father, Henry, born in 1852, came from a religious household, a family of wealthy brewers in Colchester. Henry was a boy of seven in 1859 when Darwin's 'Origin of Species' was published. At the time the newspapers were full of political speeches and the churches preached sermons on the subject of evolution, most of them stifling the scientific argument in favour of religious dogma. Henry must have caught a hint of the argument in favour of evolution and his imagination was stirred. The notion that the origins of life lay buried in the earth, in the fossilised bones or fragments of animals, plants or artefacts excited Henry so much that as a boy of eight, he found fossil stones and hid them in his bed and was whipped for his pains. A passion for prehistory dominated his life, although he dutifully qualified as an architect and civil engineer.

The couple were married in 1879. Even on their honeymoon Henry had mapped out a tour of Europe and the Near East to include sites of potential importance to prehistoric science. Charlotte, forewarned, had taken a course on field geology before her marriage and the newly-weds spent days digging in likely sites for flint implements. A year after his marriage Henry presented an erudite paper on the Ores and Minerals of Greece[4] to the British Association and later on he wrote papers on the pre-history of the Thames Valley where he had excavated a fine collection of flints.

As an architect Henry designed two breweries himself and he was interested and knowledgeable on the subject of brewing. In 1882 he wrote a paper for the British Association on the new, increased tax on beer. The only people who stood to gain from the tax, Henry concluded, were the Exchequer and the poorest section of the labouring classes, who escaped duty altogether after using only two bushels of malt. The losers were the farmers, the brewers, the maltsters he explained in the course of a technical argument. In his view "ignorant labourers . . . make very bad beer duty free . . . and spoil much costly material."[5] It would seem that as the son of a brewing family,

Henry Stopes was indulging in special pleading in a scientific paper, a practice that was not unknown to his daughter in later years.

He did convey to Marie, even as small girl, his passion for archaeology. He would take her with him on his digs, show her how to wash, label and catalogue the specimens and help her to realise that they were digging for the beginning of life. In his letters he made the past come alive for the child. He wrote to her of a "dear little baby elephant tooth" that he had found and his flints always sent their love to Marie and she sent hers back.

Marie grew up with parents, both of whom were articulate, intelligent and keen to press their arguments, convinced that by publishing and arguing in print they could change the world.

Charlotte, away too often to supervise her girls' education, decided to send them to a boarding school in her native Edinburgh when Marie was twelve. Although the school had been recommended by Suffragist friends, the Stopes considered that the education fell below their expectations. The family moved from south London to Hampstead so that the two girls could attend the North London Collegiate, then one of the two leading girls' schools in the country. The pupils at North London were encouraged to go on to University and to pursue wide interests. When they walked about in their uniform of long skirts and high-necked blouses, they swung their arms vigorously to show that they were freed from the "trammels of tradition." It was an ideal school for Marie and the making of her. She had been regarded as rather a dull student, hampered by her mother's idiosyncratic teaching methods, but at her new school she began to do well in Chemistry. The new headmistress, Dr. Sophie Bryant, a chemist and a staunch feminist, was the first woman to take a degree in science. Even Marie's holiday expeditions with her father and his fossils earned respect at her new enlightened school. When she was 16 she was elected to the Committee of the Science Club and she presented a paper on prehistoric man, illustrated with a collection of her father's flints, which was noticed favourably in the school magazine. Through Henry Stopes she met intellectuals of the calibre of Norman McColl, Editor of the *Athenaeum*, Professor Sayle, the physiologist, and Sir Francis Galton. To her teachers' surprise Marie matriculated well and sailed through university.

Marie Stopes enrolled in the Science Department of London University at the turn of the century, taking Botany as her first subject. There were, of course, very few women students in the university at the time and Marie enjoyed the freedom of mixing with young men, quite unchaperoned, and without a trace of self-consciousness. She did not think of them as her beaux but as competitors and gloried in the fact that in her work she could often outshine them. She became President of the Women's Debating Society and appalled the University authorities by introducing joint debates with the men.

Encouraged by her Professor of Botany, Professor Oliver, she even went on geological field trips with the male students, digging for specimens in the pouring rain and walking ten to fifteen miles a day, oblivious of and impervious to the possibility of impropriety.

Although she enjoyed the extracurricular activities, she worked extremely hard. She had persuaded the reluctant authorities to allow her to try to cram three years' work into two. At the age of twenty-two she gained her BSc with honours in Botany and Geology. It was a splendid result but tragically her beloved father died as she received the good news. He had been in a sense both mother and father to her and they had shared interests.

Marie plunged into postgraduate work at the university. Her fatherly professor took her on as his assistant and introduced her to the relatively new science of Paleobotany, the study of fossil plants. With Marie's unique experience of helping with archaeological excavations over the years, the new study was thrilling. She found excitement in the prospect of digging for coal balls, the chalky nodules of rock embedded in coal seams, which contained the petrified leaves, twigs, stems and seed of primitive plants millions of year old. These, in turn, could yield evidence of the reproductive system and development of plants down the ages.

Through her examination results Marie qualified for a travelling scholarship for a year's postgraduate work abroad. The Botanical Institute attached to Munich University had a Professor with a distinguished international reputation and the world's largest collection of cycads, the most primitive form of the fern-like seed-bearing plants, both fossilised and living.

Marie knew no one in the city and would be the only woman student among 500 men. Marie was twenty-three when she went to Munich, a handsome and clever girl, immensely ambitious. Her parents, both progressive intellectuals had never discussed the question of sex with her, nor even attempted to alert her to possible entanglements. The only instruction she had received at home was from her father and that had been entirely negative. He had warned her that to kiss a boy before marriage was impure and that no decent girl could consider marriage before she was twenty-five.

Marie lived in digs, worked extremely hard and played hard, visiting the opera and watching, entranced, a performance of Isadora Duncan, the dancer. During Carnival Week in the city, she enjoyed attending the masked balls, but prided herself, in her letters to her mother, on her ice-cold frigidity. In Munich, as in London, Marie proved an outstanding student and within the course of a year she became the first woman to take her PhD in Botany with honours. She wrote her thesis in German on the reproductive system of the cycads, the most primitive of seed-bearing plants.

And that was not all. Isolated, despite all her interests, she formed perhaps the most unsuitable attachment possible, to a married Japanese professor with a child, who shared her passion for Botany. Their affair was entirely platonic and they knew nothing at all of each other's background. Professor Fujii's command of English was limited and his knowledge of Western courtship and Western ways almost non-existent. Marie, of course, was completely ignorant of the culture of Japan; they were both strangers in Germany, enthusiastic and idealistic about their work. Professor Fujii, a gentle soul, instigated divorce proceedings against his already disaffected wife and went home to Japan. Before he left, they did manage one kiss. Since Fujii was as inexperienced as Marie, and as Japanese men did not indulge in the practice at the time, the result was less than thrilling. Marie however, considered herself betrothed but kept the affair a total secret.

Meanwhile she pursued her brilliant career. After Munich she was appointed assistant lecturer in Botany at Manchester University, the first woman employed in the Science Faculty. A year later, at the age of twenty-five, she gained her DSc., the youngest Doctor of Science in Britain.

Living close to the coal mines of Lancashire, Marie fulfilled her appetite for adventure by going down to the coal face herself to collect her specimens. For her the work was absorbing and thrilling. She wanted to find out why the flowering plants, angiosperms, propagated by seeds and protected by an ovary had flourished, whereas the more primitive form of plant, the fern-like gymnosperms were far rarer.

Now her work had an extra edge, as she longed to visit her lover in Japan. Among paleobotanists it was common knowledge that angio impressions had been discovered in Japan and in other countries. Marie sent off urgently to Fujii asking him to obtain specimens of rock from the Island of Hokkaido, off the north coast of Japan where, she predicted, angiosperms might be found. The specimens he sent, when sectioned, were promising. Marie Stopes, backed by her professors in London and Manchester applied to the Royal Society to finance her on a trip to Japan to discover the ancestors of the flowering plants. The undertaking was bold and original, particularly for a woman, but the scientific world wanted to find petrified angiosperms which would reveal the whole structure of the ancestor of flowering plants and perhaps the secret of its evolutionary prevalence. Her work on the reproductive system in plants was, of course, to prove of immense importance when her life changed.

The Royal Society agreed to give her a financial grant to travel to Japan. She was to be attached to the University of Tokyo, Fujii's university. Only Marie Stopes could arrange a legitimate reason to hunt for love and fossils in the same journey.

Marie arrived in Japan in August 1907. Her presence as an independent, single Western woman was a novelty and she attracted much attention. Japanese society was dominated by men and women were treated with disdain. Initially she made a magnificent field trip to the island of Hokkaido and became something of a heroine. She was in her element as she led a party of thirty men, a professor (not Fujii) who acted as interpreter, a surveyor, a Ministry of Agriculture official, a policeman and numerous coolies through the prickly forests. She was something of a tease, and at the planning stage of the journey she had worn a white muslin dress, with a pink silk sash to emphasise her femininity, while assuring the hidebound Japanese that she was able to walk for miles up a river bed and quite happy to sleep on stones. She was as good as her word, although she had sensibly changed into more practical clothes, short blue Japanese trousers and jacket, cloth leggings, stiff socks and straw sandals. She strode ahead of the party, brave and stoic, carrying only her fan and her hammer, as she scrambled up the river banks, scrabbling for her specimens. The expedition was a great success and the discoveries she made justified the Royal Society's faith in her. But on the personal side her life in Japan was a disaster. Marie discovered to her chagrin that Professor Fujii shrank from her prominence and her dominant personality, pleading illness. After eighteen months of productive scientific work Marie returned home, still a virgin and utterly miserable in her personal life.

Marie Stopes made an important contribution to Paleobotany and her work in the field is still referred to today. Her studies on the composition of coal, which she pursued for years, were published by the Royal Society in 1919. She identified the four ingredients of coal; vitrain, clairan, durain and fusain and the names are still used with modifications. A paper she wrote on Coal Balls in 1908 was quoted in an Anglo-French paper on the subject as recently as 1985.[6]

Back home in 1908, successful in her work, unhappy in love she poured out her feelings of disappointment and disillusion in poems, two novels, one unpublished, a play and her journal.

In considering Marie Stopes, the public figure, it seems to me that one could trace the debt that she owed her parents. Her awkward mother, Charlotte, had given her self-confidence as a

woman to work in the world, and she owed much to
Charlotte's incisive brain and her strong will. Marie also I
think, inherited her ambition to win fame as a literary luminary,
an ambition which eluded her to the end. To her father,
Henry, she quite clearly owed her passion for science and her
interest in the origins of life.

It was when she began to deal with her experience of
frustration and sexual deprivation that Marie came into her
own. For ten years, from the time that she returned from Japan
until 1918, she became more and more preoccupied with sex
and the longing for a child, in spite of, or perhaps because of
an unsatisfactory marriage. By 1916 she was using her research
as the source of advice, lecturing to a group of women doctors
on the female sexual drive. Finally in 1918 she found
fulfilment for a time as a woman and as a pioneer adviser on
sex and marriage. In a dramatic transformation she had turned
from observing minute, prehistoric forms of life under the
microscope to advising and actively helping millions of human
beings to find satisfaction in their intimate relationships. . . the
rest is history.

References:

[1] Vera Brittain, *Testament of Youth*, Gollancz Ltd, London, 1933.

[2] C. P. Blacker, *Guy's Hospital Gazette*, London, 1924.

[3] Charlotte Charmichael Stopes, *The Sphere of man in relation to that of Woman in the Constitution*, T. Fisher Unwin, London, 1907.

[4] H. Stopes, *Some Ores and Minerals from Laurie, Greece*, British Association for the Advancement of Science, 1881.

[5] H. Stopes, *The Influence of Beer Duty*, British Association for the Advancement of Science, 1882.

[6] A. Scott & G. Rex, *The Formation and Significance of Coal Balls*, Royal Society, London, B311, 1985.

Marie Stopes and her correspondents: Personalising population decline in an era of demographic change

Lesley A Hall

An enormous quantity of Marie Stopes' correspondence survives. In this paper I shall not be discussing her interchanges with the great and the good, which tend to consist of stomach-churningly obsequious letters to famous and influential supporters of the birth control movement and their somewhat evasive responses. Her cringe-making coy threat to the cartoonist David Low to cry "real wet tears" if he could not attend a function she was organising is particularly but not uniquely nauseating.[1] Nor shall I describe in detail her often fraught and even hostile interaction with other activists in the birth control movement, women, and some men, who perceived themselves as colleagues in the cause rather than the disciples which Marie felt they should be. I shall concentrate on one particular group from whom she received postbags full of mail: ordinary members of the general public who knew of her only through her books or from reports in the press. The historian is extremely fortunate in the survival of thousands of letters from ordinary private individuals to Stopes, covering a period from 1918 to the Second World War, and representing nearly all groups within the population. Individuals, both men

27

and women, found themselves capable of disclosing to Stopes' highly sympathetic public persona the most intimate details of their married life and its difficulties. This correspondence shows Marie Stopes in a remarkably favourable light, and I will be considering some of the reasons why this might be so.

The very positive way in which her readership responded to her works is amply demonstrated by copious comments in the letters. A couple from men: "your glorious gift of expressing the hitherto inexpressible"; "the finest and sanest books I have ever read on the subject".[2] And from women: "may God prosper your noble work . . . I felt as though I was having a heart to heart chat with you"; "your sex owes you a deep debt of gratitude for your heroic frankness".[3] A very large percentage of this correspondence was to do with birth control. I shall focus mainly on comments and queries which related to Stopes' message of "Babies in the right place", given the theme of this conference and the constraints of time, but it was only one of numerous questions to do with sex and marriage upon which correspondents sought Stopes' advice as the only source they knew for possible assistance in such a taboo area. These letters provide an almost unique insight into what the drab statistics of population decline actually meant in terms of the experiences and practices of couples during this era of demographic change.

Numerous couples were not using any form of birth control. There were many accounts similar to the following:

> I am the mother of 6 children, 5 living, oldest 10 years of age, baby 18 months.

> I'm the mother of 10 now and eight living out of them, the oldest 18 and the youngest 4 months.

15 children, 12 born alive but only 10 living now. There
   is only 12 months between some of them, two years
   is the longest.[4]

However, many couples already had some notion of limiting
their families before encountering Stopes' writings and had
already been doing something to avoid pregnancy, she was not
presenting them with an entirely new concept.

While couples and individuals were aware that artificial birth
control was a possibility, some registered profound moral
qualms, reluctance or repugnance at the concept: "such means
and devices are rather abhorrent to me"; "like many others I
have always shrunk from enquiring into these matters"; "the
idea of wearing artificial means of prevention tends to make us
question the rightness of union apart from children"; "I want to
maintain our love without degrading it by impure means".[5] One
man shrank from the idea of birth control "as from
sodomy".[6] Because of these ambivalent feelings about the whole
subject, some correspondents found it necessary to give their
credentials for daring to venture to enquire about it: "my reason
for seeking the information is not morbid curiosity. I am a
married man with one child"; "I have become convinced that
the practice of self-control in this respect without the use of
some artificial appliance, must in time prove injurious"; "I do
not want the information from a selfish motive but for my
wife's"; "the ever present fear of a woman and the mental
agony of a man lest she should have been 'caught' is one of the
foundations of marital unhappiness."[7] Working class women
seeking advice often claimed to have "done their duty" already
in bearing children.[8]

While doctors writing to Stopes sometimes differentiated the
needs of the "poor prolific wife" (deserving of contraception)[9]
from the "indiscriminate practice of control" (not a good
thing),[10] any eugenic perspective on the subject was largely

lacking in this correspondence from the general public. If they expressed any doubts about "fitness" to breed it was on their own behalf in the light of almost folkloric anxieties about health problems within the family such as epilepsy: "I do not think it would be right for me to have children. . . the gentleman who wishes to marry me suffered from epileptic fits a few years ago"; "the young lady's father suffers from fits though she is quite free from them". [11]Other causes of anxiety were tuberculosis,[12]"war neurasthenia", deafness, clubfoot, and in at least one case what sounds like congenital syphilis.[13]There was also considerable concern over the possible outcome of cousins (even second cousins) marrying, though in some cases enquirers specifically commented that there was no insanity in the family or that the family was extremely healthy.[14]   Also some men feared that they had unfitted themselves for fatherhood through practising self-abuse in youth.[15]

But such concerns about breeding were almost entirely personalised: there were no mentions of other groups who should or should not be reproducing. The comment of one correspondent about the over-breeding of the "inferior elements" was unusual and in fact came from Herbert Brewer, who though in fairly humble circumstances, was an active member of the Eugenics Society, writing to Stopes about the general implications of birth control rather than any personal difficulties.[16]

Many couples had only been able to conceive of limiting births through abstention, usually from all kinds of sexual activity: "We tried for some years a life of pretty rigid abstinence and it didn't work and only brought a decrease in happiness"; "We have had no union ever since the child was conceived over 5 years ago"; "I have by the greatest exercise of self-denial kept our family down to three, without any artificial checks but it has been a very great trial"; "My wife and I have been married three years and we have not had a union, because we do not want children yet."[17] In one case a husband had taken a job in the tinfields of Nigeria as an extreme contraceptive measure.[18] Abstention was not an easy option: one woman typically found that "my refusals have caused a barrier between us and he is not nearly so attentive and as I see now heaps of other disturbances nothing very serious but they all tend to widen the breach sprung from the same cause".[19]

When couples had been using other means to limit their families they were seldom at all happy, finding the methods available both unreliable and adversely affecting sexual pleasure. Some practised coitus interruptus/withdrawal: "I have been married 12 years and have always used the withdrawal method with success"; "I don't see any way to limit conception except by interrupted coitus. This I plead guilty to"; "I . . . have been reduced to withdrawing which I know to be bad for both and am becoming semi-impotent."[20]Men found this practice not only deleterious from their own point of view but their wife's: "I have to practice coitus interruptus which is most unsatisfactory from my wife's point of view and therefore from mine because my climax is reached as a rule just as the pleasure for her is about to begin"; "withdrawal leaves the wife 'in the air' as you say."[21] Women tended to concur, finding that it left them excited and unsatisfied and had generally adverse affects on their health and "leaves us both unsatisfied and is a strain to both of us."[22] At least one woman mentioned the belief that "holding back" her own orgasm ("restraint at the critical moment") would prevent pregnancy.[23]

Some couples employed sheaths, but these were not popular. Men wrote that: "One seems to be so conscious of their presence that as aesthetic methods they are not very desirable"; "renders the 'sex act' sordid and destroys the aesthetic side entirely"; "remind me of one having a bath with top hat and spurs on."[24] Women did not much like them either: one found that as a birth control method it had "given us great satisfaction . . . [but] I find I cannot reach to an orgasm without special help from my husband"; and another wrote "being very much in love with one another we found the sheath unsatisfactory".[25]

Chemical pessaries - "safety cones" - were known but their reliability was much doubted "Is there any truth in the statement that by law there must be at least one harmless and ineffective pessary in every box sold?"; "I am informed that so many per cent of check pessaries have to be made *defective* else the Government do not allow their sale."[26] They also sometimes caused adverse reactions in women: one woman wrote to Stopes about this, saying that "I could not bare [*sic*] to go to a doctor" - it is not clear whether this was general reluctance to consult a male doctor about a gynaecological problem or fear of revealing use of contraception.[27] Douching was also known of, though at least one woman who had practised this found it harmful.[28] There was an occasional, usually inaccurate, concept of a safe period: "there is *only* danger I understand when or about the menses."[29]

One man wrote to Stopes: "I was a short time since in the flat in London of a fashionable cocotte . . . was informed that middle-aged married men came to cocottes as a means of keeping down their progeny! So you see that there are other means of birth control!"[30] While some correspondents queried whether birth control were "not a form of prostitution",[31] this is presumably not what they meant. Some couples simply refrained from actual penetration, managing to satisfy themselves by "other means" which appears to have meant mutual masturbation or intra-crural intercourse,[32] or by a practice described as "extra-vaginal intercourse."[33] Anal intercourse as a contraceptive alternative was extremely seldom considered by Stopes' correspondents.[34]

The idea that women could not conceive while breast-feeding was still to be found. American birth control historian Janet Farrell Brodie suggests that prolonged lactation certainly affects population growth at a statistical level, but she is somewhat more sceptical about its efficacy in the context of the requirements of the individual woman or couple. Lactation affects different women in different ways, and its contraceptive influence varies according to "how long a woman breast feeds, on when her menstruation resumes after childbirth, and on how long and how often the infant suckles".[35] Under the stringent Truby King rules of fixed four-hourly feeds current in the 1920s it was unlikely to prove efficacious. One couple, "repeatedly told by different persons that a woman cannot conceive while she is breastfeeding an infant", were "sadder and wiser persons."[36]

The occasional very bizarre notion of a contraceptive method was put forward: in at least one case dependent on total misconception about the reproductive system. The letter itself does not survive, but Stopes replied "In reply to your question about rendering of the navel air-tight as a possible means of preventing conception I may say I never heard anything more ridiculous in my life. It is an absolutely preposterous notion."[37] There is, however, other evidence for this belief that sealing the navel had a contraceptive effect, Maureen Sutton's oral history study of Lincolnshire women's beliefs about sex during a similar period, *We Didn't Know Aught*, mentions a vicar's wife whose notion of contraception was "sticking plaster over her belly button".[38]

Withdrawal, abstention, and the sheath were all methods demanding male co-operation. There were, however, women who felt that they could not trust their husbands and therefore needed to take precautions themselves, as a unilateral measure: "my husband likes drink and will not be careful so it rests with me to look out for myself"; "my husband is so selfish he doesn't care so long as he gets what he wants what you suffer makes no differences to him in Fack he is a Rotter".[39] One mother wrote on behalf of a daughter married to a "handsom but very rof farmer who treats her very indiferently," who would not practice abstinence as the mother recommended.[40] A widow had "tried various forms of birth control" during her not very happy marriage in order "to avoid a large family for which I had to earn much of the living"[41]

While the contraceptive cap as recommended by Stopes was often regarded as an up-to-date, unobtrusive and reliable contraceptive, not all women found it easy to fit. One woman had problems because of a very long vagina, and had even got "my Hubbie" to endeavour to insert it, another one, unable to fit the cap herself, could not bring herself to go to a local doctor and sought Stopes' personal assistance.[42] Others did not entirely trust it: sometimes because they had already experienced failure, as in the case of one couple who had subsequently reverted to the sheath.[43] Others did not trust the way it had been fitted: one woman, fitted by the "Union for Distributing Birth Control" (possibly a commercial concern?), wrote to Stopes for reassurance about the reliability of the method, since otherwise "The only thing left is to deny my husband the satisfaction of his emotions, and you will understand how this also hurts me".[44]

Some men, although keen for their wives to employ the cap and relieve themselves from the nerve-wracking strain of coitus interruptus or using disliked condoms, found their wives resistant, which may, of course have to do with the dynamics of that particular marriage: "[My wife] said [the check pessary] was distasteful and took away the romance of everything . . .

the more I think of this matter the more I think it looks selfish on the woman's part especially if coitus interruptus really does harm to the man"; "I took my wife to you in order to be fitted for an occlusive cap (very much against her will) as I considered it would be a more efficient and beneficial method of birth control".[45] However most men seem to have been rather more sensitive to their spouse's feelings, seeking advice "since my wife feels that the method recommended would be repellent".[46]

Abortion has often been regarded as even more subterranean a practice than birth control. Nevertheless a vast number of requests for abortion advice were received (much to her horror) by Stopes. These were mostly from women, though a significant number came from men, suggesting that it was an issue in which both members of the couple were concerned, though the brunt of anxiety and suffering fell upon the woman. Most of these requests concerned unwanted pregnancy within marriage, when there were already too many children or conceptions following too closely upon one another or the wife suffering from ill health, rather than from the desperate unmarried, though there were a few of these: for example the woman, three months pregnant and alone in the world with no family, who wrote "the young man I am in that condition to sailed 5 weeks ago for New Zealand. I'm absolutely demented and would do anything for to know what to do".[47]

Women often expressed requests for assistance in terms of "bringing on" periods: "my monthly illness has stopped for 2 months you might be able to advise me what to do to bring it away again"; "surely there must be some way of bringing on the periods with safety when one is not so very far gone".[48] The use of abortifacients was mentioned in some letters: "I have heard that a medicine of some kind is allowed to be given to stop things at the early stages"; "Are we doing wrong in taking these pills?"; "My wife has been trying Vegetable Tablets".[49] The general ignorance, when it came to practicalities, of what could be done, is very apparent: "We are ignorant of how to deal with such cases"; "the problem [is] how to effect menstruation in my wife, who is overdue by about a fortnight."[50] Presumably it was those couples who did not have access to any network which might have put them in touch with an abortionist who wrote to Stopes, but in at least one case the husband wrote "My wife will not speak to anyone."[51] The terror and sense of disgrace which affected couples faced with undesired pregnancy was eloquently described "I am afraid I shall lose her if she has another child and she is so frightened herself. I feel afraid to go out to work and leave her. I would give all I possess to have her right again".[52]

These letters give a powerful sense of the deep fears and feelings around unwanted pregnancy and the anxieties and ignorance of many individuals around how to prevent it. They reveal that couples were engaging in a range of strategies to do so but that in many cases these were perceived as either inefficacious, distasteful, nerve-wracking or all three.

Although there were these thousands and thousands for whom another child was a feared, intolerable burden, to be avoided at all costs, there were also those who desperately longed for children who did not come, and many letters in the Stopes collection reflect this other side of her work for "babies in the right place". Some couples were completely childless: one woman had been married for 7 years and undergone an operation but still had no luck.[53] Another, married barely a year, was anxious about her inability to conceive: "we have frequent unions but my husband seems to think not proper unions . . . what I notice after each union, it so quickly flows from me again"; another woman similarly believed her failure to conceive was "after an intercourse the fluid always appears to escape" although her doctor had told her that her womb was too small.[54] In some cases there were obvious sexual problems within the marriage, as when the husband "cannot get in the full state he should" therefore they had not had "the pleasure of one perfect union". In another case the husband had been for three years in poor health, during which they had "at intervals attempted intercourse, but I have always known that it couldn't have been the real thing . . . I should rather like to have a child."[55] Others had succeeded in conceiving but had lost the child, as with one woman unwilling to resign herself to childlessness after a stillbirth and medical advice that her kidney condition made further childbearing inadvisable.[56] There were also those who did have children but not as many as they would have liked. One woman of 36, with a husband of 60, had two children but would have liked more.[57] A woman with two sons aged 18 and 20 was anxious to have another child.[58]

In some cases the reason for the lack of children was that the couple was not having sex, or at least, not coital sex capable of leading to impregnation. A surprising number of Stopes' correspondents had unconsummated marriages: "We have not yet had a normal sex union"; "We are both healthy and clean-minded but up to now we have made a complete mess of things"; "When we come together I have never succeeded in making entry. . . I am a strong working fellow"; "Entry being so very difficult and it took so little trying on my part to cause such pain."[59] Sometimes this was a long-standing state of affairs: "I am 54 years of age my wife being 48 and although we have been married many years, union between us has never been possible"; "We have been married just over 12 years and yet . . . we have not been able to consummate our marriage."[60] and other lengthy periods mentioned included 5, 9, and 10 years.[61]

Even couples who did manage to consummate their marriages did not necessarily do so very effectively. Marie Stopes received many cries for help from men and women to relieve their ignorance and sexual ineptitude. Women married in complete ignorance about the sexual act: one, who had been a teacher, wrote "my first few days of married life was a nightmare" even though she had married "one of the dearest of men".[62] Many men who had kept themselves "pure" for their wives suffered from over-intense sexual feeling once they were married: "I have never yet got the penis in more than 1 inch or so until it's ejaculated."[63] Some men found that union hurt the wife, and feared that this was due to disproportion in the size of their genital organs: "I suppose it is because I am much larger made than most men?"[64] Some had problems working out the position in which the act should be accomplished: "Although I have read several books on the subject I have never yet learnt what is considered the natural position to adopt during union", or else they found that "the ordinary position . . . is much too tiring and exhausting for her."[65]

Few doctors were prepared to advise on or fit birth control devices. Very much the reverse, according to the many grim tales told by Stopes' correspondents respecting their attempts to seek medical advice on birth control. A number reported outright refusal to give such advice: "He refused to advise me on the subject, perhaps because he was uncertain himself"; "My doctor is the old-fashioned sort who warned me not to use preventives you know the sort".[66] Others reported dire warnings: "We have been told by a doctor that the use of preventive methods may endanger the probability of children when we do want them".[67] Other doctors had vague or contradictory ideas about methods of birth control and their advice could not be relied on: "My doctor knows nothing or very little on the subject".[68] Much more common, however, were cases in which a medical man advised patients that they should have no more children, without making any mention of birth control. Stopes received many plaints similar to the following: "Our doctor advised me strongly at this time that it would be very unwise for her to have any more children at this time on account of her health, he did not, however, give me any practical advice".[69]

While it might be supposed that, even though doctors were generally unsympathetic to birth control, they would have been rather more helpful over problems of infertility, couples found little joy in consulting doctors about such difficulties. Some doctors were unwilling to do anything to assist infertile couples: "We had a talk with our own doctor but he appeared unwilling to speak about it so we did not pursue the matter further".[70] Most doctors regarded it as the wife's "fault" and suggested that she undergo surgery. The male factor in a sterile marriage could be discovered readily by non-invasive means, examining his semen to see if it were potent, most doctors however were unwilling to accept that responsibility for barrenness might lie with the husband. One husband wrote to Stopes in 1931 that only after several operations on his wife did the doctor test his semen, and had not even known that this was possible.[71] One woman reported that her husband had seen two doctors neither of whom had suggesting examining his semen: the husband was "strongly of the opinion that medical men know little about sex troubles."[72]

How did Marie Stopes respond to this massive influx of heart-rending correspondence? She had invited her readers to communicate with her in connection with her theories about female sexual periodicity, but she surely did not anticipate the sack-loads of mail that arrived from desperate couples and individuals who felt that here, finally, was someone who could answer questions they had never dared to ask indeed, prior to reading her books, had barely been able to formulate. She did her best to help by giving them the benefit of her wide knowledge about sexual matters and her expertise in birth control - as she put it in the Preface to *Married Love*, she had "paid such a terrible price for sex ignorance that I feel that knowledge gained at such a cost should be placed at the service of humanity".[73] However, the amount of correspondence soon became far too great for one woman to answer and she had to hire secretaries and rely on the assistance of her husband, Humphrey Verdon Roe. Even so, she did not totally delegate the responsibility and continued to read incoming letters and to annotate them with suggestions, as well as sometimes adding a personal postscript to a form letter or even replying herself if she found a case particularly interesting or complex, even sometimes making herself available to individuals.[74]

In 1920 Marie wrote to Havelock Ellis that she could contemplate publishing "'Letters to Marie Stopes', every one containing a pretty revelation of doctors' incompetence!".[75] However, in practice she went to some lengths to build up a list of doctors who could be depended upon to provide advice and information along lines she approved to whom she could refer enquirers. In 1919 she wrote to Dr E. B. Turner in connection with one "particularly difficult" type of enquirer: "the man, deeply in love . . . suffering from excessively premature ejaculation". She added "I shrink from thrusting them back into the arms of the profession in general, as in a number of cases they have already despaired of medical help."[76] In 1920 she wrote to Dr Jane Hawthorne on the recommendation of Mrs Bayley of Harley Street, hoping that she might have found what I have long sought for - a lady doctor to whom I could send some of the many women who write to me for simple healthful advice concerning the use of the small cap pessary or other methods of birth control, and also for examination in some of their marital difficulties.[77]

As a result she frequently advised correspondents to "go and see Dr Jane L. Hawthorne . . . She is a very nice lady doctor and in sympathy with my views".[78]

There may have been a degree of compromise involved here. There were very few clinics and they were aimed at poor women: as Marie wrote to one enquirer "Your friend should make an appointment to see our dear Dr Fisher at the Clinic - of course she can come free anytime, but then may have to wait in turn with poor mothers, so I expect she'd rather have an appointment".[79] A similar realism led Stopes to recommend Lamberts as a reliable source of supply for contraceptive appliances, with the proviso that "I do not like giving them this advertisement but feel that in the interests of humanity failure should not be allowed to arise through the use of inferior appliances of which there are many on the market".[80]

Stopes' helpfulness even went as far as describing the abdominal exercises which she felt would be helpful for one woman's condition.[81] She was also prepared to reveal sometimes in private correspondence things that she would not have stated publicly. She had a personal set of recommendations for the treatment of menstrual irregularity: "if you have been irregular or fear irregularity through overwork etc, you should take a hot bath the night before the period is due and just one dose of quinine two or three days before the period is due".[82] She was even prepared in some cases to advocate abortion, or, as she preferred to put it, the evacuation of the uterus.

One woman who had become pregnant whilst possibly infected with venereal disease, was advised by Marie in 1920 to "at once go to the doctor who . . . gave instructions that you

must not have children for two years owing to the presence of
venereal disease, and . . . [a]sk him to evacuate the uterus,
which it will be his social duty to do under the proper
recognised conditions. If by any incredible chance he does not
do so, please communicate with me, and let me have his name
and I will have the matter followed up". The doctor did in fact
refuse, and did not respond to Stopes' irate letter, and the
woman in question later wrote that having failed to obtain an
abortion after consulting several doctors, she was under
specialist treatment in the hope of having a healthy child.[83]

There was a similar case in 1930. A lady and her husband
wrote that their doctor had told the wife that she should not
have a baby on account of her severe rheumatism. When she
did get pregnant the doctor implied that he would organise an
abortion on medical grounds but in the event failed to do so.
Marie Stopes advised them to contact Norman Haire, the Harley
Street gynaecologist, and it would seem that they did so and
that he was able to procure them an abortion.[84] She referred
another woman to Haire in 1930, though via his Cromer Street
Welfare Centre rather than his private practice, writing "if you
are ill and fear it will kill you as you say, the medical
profession are then permitted to have the evacuation of the
uterus, which would be quite safe and proper for you".[85] This
suggests that although Marie was publicly implacably hostile to
abortion, she was prepared to countenance it on health
grounds, provided it was not merely regarded as an alternative
to contraception. It is also possible that she felt particularly
sympathetic in cases of ambivalent or contradictory behaviour
on the part of doctors.

Her response to those concerned about their "fitness" for
marriage or parenthood was also more sympathetic than might
be supposed. Sometimes she addressed vague anxieties with a
bracing recommendation to "Don't let yourself be deprived by

fears which may prove groundless".[86] Fearful young men were reassured that "After two or three months of normal marriage you will cured of this debility";[87] though one at least was recommended to see Dr Turner for examination and advice.[88]

She was even moderately encouraging to those who feared various eugenic dangers. In the case of cousin marriage, while stipulating that "cases . . . have to be decided on individual merits", she suggested that provided that the families in questions were "sound", and had no "special weakness or disease", the couple could certainly "risk having one or perhaps two children". And she was quite firm that whatever their heredity, if the couple loved one another they should marry: "you will make yourselves better citizens and healthier people" even if they remained childless.[89] The young man with deafness in the family was reassured that as he was marrying "a quite normal women", she considered it "reasonably fair to the child to risk having one", but to wait for a second until quite sure of the first's being all right.[90] However, the man with an epileptic mother was advised not to have children, though marriage with the careful use of birth control was recommended.[91]

On the whole, this correspondence shows Stopes in a good light, although there were times when she could be rather sharp with enquirers, for example the man to whom she wrote in 1936 "It has taken a three-hundred page book to deal with the points you raise in your letter" and advised him to read it. In spite of this, a later letter from the same man expressed his own and his wife's gratitude for referring them to the work.[92]

One of the reasons for her benign and helpful attitude to enquirers was perhaps that the general public was responding to the books and the public persona rather than the often difficult private personality. They were perceiving Marie as she would have liked to be seen, even, perhaps, as she saw herself. Certainly the positive comments many made on her situation in

her libel-suit against Halliday Sutherland, treating her as a
martyr in a good cause, must have been gratifying. Her public
were in no sense competitors. This must have been reassuring
to an intensely competitive woman, an aspect which comes out
in occasional comments: she wrote scathingly to several
correspondents about the claims of Mrs Monteith Erskine to be
able to guarantee children of the desired sex, e.g. "The book
on sex determination by Mrs Erskine is an absolute scandal as it
is quite untrue that we can control sex in this way, and it is
very harmful for the future of the child to have the mother
hankering for the sex different from that which Nature may
have preordained."[93] While as a scientist she may have been
legitimately appalled at Mrs Erskine's theories there seems also
to have been a element of scorn for a rival sex-guru. Even
worse vituperation was poured on the National Birth Control
Association: a correspondence of 1936 began with a woman
approaching Marie about setting up a local birth control clinic,
but then deciding to affiliate to the NBCA rather than Marie's
Society for Constructive Birth Control: the final letter, from
Marie's private secretary, reads "very sorry indeed that you
think it does not matter what kind of birth control advice is
given to the poor you are trying to help."[94]

This correspondence reveals that Marie could be more
flexible and compassionate than she is usually given credit for.
She was prepared in private correspondence to go a lot further
than she was prepared to go "on the record". This reflects her
acute sense of public persona. She had a very delicate
apprehension of where exactly the line of acceptability was and
to be able to go right up to it without ever crossing it. Her
contemporary, Alec Craig, acknowledged her capacity to
convey "to a wide audience the maximum amount of sex
education possible" while knowing when it was necessary to
resort to "reticence and inexplicitness".[95] But she was also, as

has been demonstrated, prepared to live up to the image her readers had of her as a guiding light of knowledge in a dark maze of sexual ignorance.

References:

[1] David Low papers in the Beinecke Library, Yale University, GEN MSS 96, 5/223.

[2] Marie Stopes papers in the Contemporary Medical Archives Centre, Wellcome Institute for the History of Medicine (CMAC): PP/MCS/A.190 FN, A.184 FGM.

[3] CMAC:PP/MCS/A.212 Mrs AR, A.249 Mrs MW.

[4] CMAC: PP/MCS/A.322 Mrs ED, Mrs SD, Mrs JD.

[5] CMAC: PP/MCS/A.235 Lt-Col DCT, A.211 RHR, A.153 AK (and wife), A.140 TSJ.

[6] CMAC: PP/MCS/A.15 A.

[7] CMAC: PP/MCS/A.135 WH, A.139 JSI, A.128 FH, A.131 GFH.

[8] Claire Davey, "Birth Control in Britain during the Inter-War Years: evidence from the Stopes correspondence", *Journal of Family History*, 1988. Vol 13, no 3, pp 329-345.

[9] Stopes papers in the Department of Manuscripts, British Library (BL), Additional Manuscripts 58562.

[10] CMAC: PP/MCS/A.263 WED.

[11] CMAC: PP/MCS/A.243 MEW, A.190 FAN, also A.98 AHG, A.180 HBM.

[12] CMAC: PP/MCS/A.172 AAM, A.206 JR, A.250 GEW, A.70 FED, A.2 Mr A.

[13] CMAC: PP/MCS/A.1/23, Anonymous correspondent (male), A.230 AWT, A.67 Mr C, A.70 FED.

[14] CMAC: PP/MCS/A.221 WES, A.232 RSST, A.64 HAC, A.35 FB, A.58 WC, A.173 Capt EM.

[15] CMAC: PP/MCS/A.182 JRPM, A.17 WDB, A.19 RB.

[16] CMAC: PP/MCS/A.39 Herbert Brewer to Marie Stopes, 1925.

[17] CMAC: PP/MCS/A.183 Capt RCM, A.148 RHK, A.147 CEGJ, A.89 ABF.

[18] CMAC: PP/MCS/A.249 DRFSW .

[19]CMAC: PP/MCS/A.248 Mrs CGMW.

[20]CMAC: PP/MCS/A.209 AR, A.198 CKP, A.168 Capt EM.

[21]CMAC: PP/MCS/A.168 Lt-Col WSMN, A.145 EYJ.

[22]CMAC: PP/MCS/A.169 Mrs RMacL, PP/MCS/A.248 Mrs AW.

[23]CMAC:PP/MCS/A.212 Mrs SLR.

[24]CMAC: PP/MCS/A.171 GEM, A.145 AJJ, A.46 JB.

[25]CMAC: PP/MCS/A.114 Mrs MTH, A.115 Mrs RH.

[26]CMAC: PP/MCS/A.187 Lt-Cdr RN, A.247 Capt JWW, A.206 HFR.

[27]CMAC: PP/MCS/A.168 Mrs D Mack.

[28]CMAC: PP/MCS/A.247 Mrs SW.

[29]CMAC: PP/MCS/A.234 MT.

[30]CMAC: PP/MCS/A.128 EH.

[31]CMAC: PP/MCS/A.14 HLA.

[32]CMAC: PP/MCS/A.113 HFG.

[33]CMAC: PP/MCS/A.202 WP.

[34]CMAC: PP/MCS/A.15 SSA, A.66 GSC.

[35]Janet Farrell Brodie, *Contraception and Abortion in Nineteenth-Century America*, Cornell University Press, 1994, pp. 47-8.

[36]CMAC: PP/MCS/A.246 Mrs W, A.247 Mrs DW.

[37]CMAC: PP/MCS/A.189 FSN.

[38]Maureen Sutton, *'We Didn't Know Aught': A Study of Sexuality, Superstition and Death in Women's Lives in Lincolnshire during the 1930s, '40s and '50s*, Paul Watkins, Stamford, Lincs, 1992 p. 2.

[39]CMAC: PP/MCS/A.247 Mrs W, A.170 Mrs McQ.

[40] CMAC: PP/MCS/A.213 letter received via Dr Maude Royden.

[41]CMAC: PP/MCS/A.116 Mrs FLH.

[42]CMAC: PP/MCS/A.118 Mrs DH, A.170 Mrs JM.

[43]CMAC: PP/MCS/A.115 Mrs RH.

[44]CMAC: PP/MCS/A.119 Mrs IH.

[45]CMAC: PP/MCS/A.196 TRP, A.153 KSK.

[46]CMAC: PP/MCS/A.189 AGN.

[47]CMAC: PP/MCS/A.167 Miss LMcG.

[48]CMAC: PP/MCS/A.118 Mrs CH, A.115 Mrs RH.

[49]CMAC: PP/MCS/A.179 WEM, A.166 BWMcM, A.89 F.

[50]CMAC: PP/MCS/A.182 GM, A.160 AEL.

[51]CMAC: PP/MCS/A.182 GM.

[52]CMAC: PP/MCS/A.182 GM.

[53]CMAC: PP/MCS/A.214 Mrs GPR.

[54]CMAC: PP/MCS/A.245 Mrs GMW, A.116 Mrs NH.

[55]CMAC: PP/MCS/A.244 Mrs AW, A.167 Mrs MMcD.

[56]CMAC: PP/MCS/A.213 Mrs CER.

[57]CMAC: PP/MCS/A.245 Mrs RW.

[58]CMAC: PP/MCS/A.245 Mrs DW.

[59]CMAC: PP/MCS/A.28 BFB, A.80 SGE, A.179 EJM, A.252 GSY.

[60]CMAC: PP/MCS/A.222 AFS, A.250 CCW.

[61]CMAC: PP/MCS/A.180 GM, A.152 Mrs CEK, A.147 Mrs MJ.

[62]CMAC: PP/MCS/A.114 Mrs EH.

[63]CMAC: PP/MCS/A.168 Mr RJMcK.

[64]CMAC: PP/MCS/A.97 G-F.

[65]CMAC: PP/MCS/A.178 LM, A.109 JMGG.

[66]CMAC: PP/MCS/A.246 HPW, A.212 HCR.

[67]CMAC: PP/MCS/A.121 JH.

[68]CMAC: PP/MCS/A.48 AHRB.

[69]CMAC: PP/MCS/A.94 GF.

[70]CMAC: PP/MCS/A.152 JK.

[71]CMAC: PP/MCS/A.36 Mr B.

[72]CMAC: PP/MCS/A.127 Mrs MH.

[73]Marie Carmichael Stopes, *Married Love: A New Contribution to the Solution of Sex Difficulties*, first published London: A. C. Fifield Ltd, 1918, 'Author's Preface', p. xiii.

[74]CMAC: PP/MCS/A.247 Mrs EDW.

[75]CMAC: PP/MCS/A.265.

[76]BL Add Mss 58565.

[77]CMAC: PP/MCS/A.272 Stopes to Dr Jane Hawthorne 27 Apr 1920.

[78]CMAC: PP/MCS/A.36 Mr HB.

[79]CMAC: PP/MCS/A.39 Mrs JB.

[80]CMAC: PP/MCS/A.37 Mrs IB.

[81]CMAC: PP/MCS/A.42 Mrs MB.

[82]CMAC: PP/MCS/A.36 Mrs HB.

[83]CMAC: PP/MCS/A.42 JB 1920.

[84]CMAC: PP/MCS/A.117 Mrs H-P 1930.

[85]CMAC: PP/MCS/A.42 Mrs RB.

[86]CMAC: PP/MCS/A.231 WJRT.

[87]CMAC: PP/MCS/A.182 JM.

[88]CMAC: PP/MCS/A.182 ESM.

[89]CMAC: PP/MCS/A.16 JES, A.233 RSST.

[90]CMAC: PP/MCS/A.230 AWT.

[91]CMAC: PP/MCS/A.181 HBM.

[92]CMAC: PP/MCS/A.41 GAB.

[93]CMAC: PP/MCS/A.42 Mrs DFB.

[94]CMAC: PP/MCS/A.39 Mrs NBM.

[95]Alec Craig, *Above All Liberties*, London: Allen and Unwin. 1942, p. 103.

The Galton Lecture 1996:
Marie Stopes, Eugenics and the Birth Control Movement

Richard A Soloway

The first birth control clinic in Britain came perilously close to being established not by Marie Stopes in 1921, but a year earlier by an American, Margaret Sanger. The two women had met in 1915 when Sanger had fled to Europe to escape charges of obscenity for publishing birth control information in contravention of the notorious Comstock Act. At the time Stopes informed her new friend that she had "long felt that the *realities* of sex were the *most* urgent subject of scientific research, and she was "just finishing a book on the intimate marriage relation which will probably electrify this country."[1] Years later when the two had become bitter rivals, and mutual terms of endearment had given way to cutting insults, Sanger recalled that when she first met her Stopes "had never heard the words birth control [which Sanger had coined in 1914] and told me that she had no knowledge of contraceptive technique." [2]

By the time Sanger returned to England in 1920, Stopes had emerged as the best known and most dynamic advocate of birth control in the country. She and her new husband, Humphrey Verdon Roe, had already begun to look for suitable quarters to open the first birth control clinic in "the British Empire" and was therefore distressed to learn that Sanger, unable to overcome legal impediments to a birth control clinic in New York, intended to establish one in London.[3]

Whether Stopes' warnings about the difficulties of finding an appropriate facility, or the cautiousness of Sanger's friends in the Malthusian League proved decisive, Sanger decided against the project. Nine months later on 17 March, 1921, the Mother's Clinic opened quietly and without ceremony - a rarity where Marie Stopes was concerned - in a house in the impoverished area of Holloway in North London.[4]

But Marie Stopes came to birth control and the opening of the Mother's Clinic not out of any fervent compassion for the suffering of the poor, nor, despite her membership in the Malthusian League, from a desire to end the age-old curse of poverty. What seemed to motivate her was a fascination with female sexuality and eugenics. *Married Love*, which launched her extraordinary career in 1918, grew out of Stopes' elaborate efforts to reconstruct her virginity after her first marriage, at the age of thirty-one, proved sexually unsatisfying - she claimed unconsummated - and was annulled after five years. In the sensational preface to *Married Love* she explained how her innocence and ignorance about sex combined to leave her unaware of the reasons for her inexplicable longings and dissatisfaction with her marriage, and led her to the British Museum. There, by reading Havelock Ellis, Edward Carpenter and others, she unravelled the mystery, unloaded her inadequate husband and began writing a scientific study of "the realities of sex" to spare other women the anguish she had endured.[5]

Stopes was certainly prone to creating her own realities and romantic fantasies, and as an accomplished paleobotanist, with doctoral degrees from Munich and the University of London, she probably knew a great deal more about coal and fossils than she did about sex when she hurriedly, almost desperately married in 1911 Reginald Gates, a man she had only known for six months. But as June Rose has revealed in her insightful biography, Gates' testimony about the marriage, deposited in the British Library after his death in 1962, indicates that while he was admittedly inexperienced and clumsy, the newlyweds were soon having intercourse frequently enough "to satisfy a normal woman" and were using condoms, which he disliked, as well as pessaries.[6]

Whether or not Stopes was, as Gates claimed, "supersexed to a degree which was almost pathological", *Married Love* was, for the time, a shockingly explicit, if cloyingly romantic, exploration of the emotional and physical aspects of sex its author alleged were absent in her own marriage. The publicity obtained from her claim of being a 'virgin' wife undoubtedly helped to popularise the work, while it also permitted her to marry Humphrey Roe, as a 'virgin' bride a few months after its publication and astounding success. Though often suggestive and tantalisingly oblique in places, *Married Love* depicted women as sexual creatures, capable of ardour, passion and desire. It provided a reasonably sensible, if somewhat idiosyncratic explanation of sexual physiology and psychology, stressing the need for understanding, sensitivity, admiration and respect in the pursuit of mutual orgasmic satisfaction. Ideal marriages were depicted as candid and honest relationships in which women were encouraged to fulfil their sexual and individual potential within an expanded setting of enlightened, companionate matrimony.[7]

Contraception made it all possible. Married couples had to be free to satisfy their natural sexual desires in harmony with the female monthly cycle, and without the fear of unwanted pregnancies hanging over them. Children needed to be spaced so as not to threaten the health, economic well-being, and physical and mental independence that women, in particular, required. Although she dwelt at length on the sexually liberating advantages of birth control, the only practical advice

Stopes provided was a brief reference to the use of vinegar and water or a quinine solution.[8]

As *Married Love* sold by the thousands and went through seven editions in its first year, its author was inundated with requests for more specific advice about the restrictive practices alluded to in the chapter on "Children." *Wise Parenthood*, which appeared a few months later, as "A Sequel to Married Love," was Stopes' response. While she still rhapsodised upon the ethereal joys of compatible sexuality and described the beneficial nutritional qualities derived from the bodily fluids released during intercourse, she also recommended as contraceptives a small occlusive rubber cap and a quinine vaginal suppository. According to Stopes, they caused the least interference with the commingling of these salubrious fluids and the maximum contact of the sex organs, necessary for mutual orgasm. They also had the added advantage of permitting women to control their own fertility while protecting them from dependency upon their husband's erratic powers of self control. Both devices she believed could be purchased from a local chemist and self-fitted. If not, she recommended, naively, a visit to the doctor.[9]

Although most of Stopes' practical birth control work in the interwar years was directed at working class wives, the majority of her writings were geared toward socially and, she believed, genetically more elevated audiences. When she did write for working class women, as in *A Letter to Working Mothers* (1919), most of the erotic passages disappeared and the romance of sexual fulfilment was replaced by harsh descriptions of the physical hardship and economic deprivation endured by the exhausted, unhealthy mothers of too many children. They were bluntly warned of the dangers and illegality of abortion, of which Stopes had a horror, and urged to purchase for two or three shillings the small rubber cap she recommended. If these were too expensive or impractical, she proposed a sponge impregnated with soap powder or "the wife's friend," a soluble quinine suppository.[10]

Once again Stopes was not very helpful or realistic with her suggestions that chemists, district nurses, or medical officers of health would readily dispense the recommended contraceptives. Exhortations to poor women to "be brave" and persistent were not about to overcome the resistance of local health officials or the ignorance, indifference or hostility of physicians.[11] She was quickly persuaded by the reaction to her proposals that if she relied on the public health community or the medical profession, the country would soon be overrun with another generation of sickly, unwanted children. The decision to go ahead with a clinic at the urging of her husband and along lines that he had laid out during the war, was in large measure motivated by the conviction that the facility would serve as a model of what could be accomplished at the local level at minimum cost.   Eventually, they correctly predicted, public authorities and even the new Ministry of Health would recognise the benefits to public health and racial improvement that would result from the establishment of similar facilities in ante-natal clinics and infant welfare centres throughout the country.[12]

Stopes' legendary conflicts with other voluntary clinics and the birth control organisations that followed in her wake were, without question, in large part a result of her inordinate need for recognition and need to dominate, as well as her constitutional inability to cooperate and share credit or authority, particularly with doctors whose qualifications and pretensions she disdained.[13] She never wavered in her conviction that the nearly seventy additional voluntary clinics that had been established by 1939 were superfluous, as was the umbrella National Birth Control Association and its successor, the Family Planning Association with which nearly all of the clinics, except hers, were affiliated. As far as Stopes was concerned, they merely diverted attention and scarce resources from the true solution to providing birth control instruction for the poor - publicly financed, local facilities based upon the model and methods scientifically proven at the Mother's Clinic.

If Stopes' general interest in birth control was a logical consequence of her romantic preoccupation with compatible sexuality within blissful marriage, her particular efforts to provide birth control for the poor had far more to do with her eugenic concerns about the impending "racial darkness" that the adoption of contraception promised to illuminate. She was a eugenicist long before she became a birth controller, joining the Eugenics Society in 1912, only five years after its founding and five years before she joined, briefly, the much older Malthusian League.[14] Although she soon resigned in a swirl of mutual recriminations from the latter organisation and in 1921 formed her own Society for Constructive Birth and Racial Progress (CBC), she remained, despite an often strained and wary relationship, a life-long member of the Eugenics Society and left it a handsome legacy, her clinics and extensive library. Her ties to eugenics, she claimed, went back to her precocious childhood when she read Darwin and met and carried on a stimulating conversation with his cousin Sir Francis Galton, an acquaintance of her naturalist father.[15]

While it was the Malthusian League that endorsed and helped promote *Wise Parenthood* and *A Letter to Working Mothers* Stopes was more eager for the approbation of the Eugenics Education Society (as it was then called) with its membership of respectable and even prominent people in science, medicine, literature and the church. She manipulated friends to get her works reviewed in the *Eugenics Review* and then was furious when the notices were more critical or superficial than she anticipated.[16] Her writings, after all, were predicated to a large degree upon an orthodox vision of procreative class eugenics that had emerged before and during the First World War. Stopes complained in *Wise Parenthood* of the large number of "unfit weaklings and diseased individuals" who threaten the race . . ." and of "the less thrifty and conscientious" who bred rapidly and produced children "weakened and handicapped by physical as well as mental warping and weakness . . ."[17] *A Letter to Working Mothers* was a practical guide, she thought, to reversing this trend.

In conformity with the wartime policy of the Eugenics Education Society, Stopes decried the dysgenic consequences of the conflict in which "all the fine, clean strong young men . . . who go out to be killed . . . have no sons to carry on the race, but . . . the cowards and unhealthy ones who remain behind can all have wives and children."[18] In subsequent years she continued to be exercised about the dysgenic, differential birth-rate with its proliferation of the low-grade C3 population while the heavily taxed, fitter A1 classes had to reduce their families in order to support the unfit.[19] Making this point in 1919 as a member of the second National Birth Rate Commission, Stopes argued that the problem was not too many people, as the neo-Malthusians believed, but too many children being born to the poor, and not enough to the wealthy. As a solution she favoured birth control for the poor and compulsory sterilisation for those too defective and irresponsible to follow her advice.[20]

To Stopes' disgust and fury the Commission ignored her recommendations and in its 1920 report backed away from an earlier neutral position on birth control to reject the safety and reliability of all known contraceptives. Her testimony, however, reflected the blend of negative and positive eugenics that was at the core of her evolving ideas of "constructive birth control," which involved not only the "repression of lives which ought not to be started, but the bringing into the world of healthy, happy, desired babies."[21] These ideas were developed more fully in what was perhaps her most eugenical book, *Radiant Motherhood* (1920) in which she described the pleasures of planned conception, healthy pregnancy and the rearing of racially fit children by highly evolved parents in a eugenically conscious world.

Though the avoidance of motherhood was unnatural, it was also a duty and a privilege that the community should restrict to healthy and genetically well-endowed parents, the most exceptional of whom might well have six children, or even more, to society's advantage. Unfortunately, she noted, the "best" and "thriftiest" of couples could only afford one or two while society "allows the diseased, the racially negligent, the thriftless, the careless, the feeble-minded, the very lowest and worst members of the community, to produce innumerable tens of thousands of stunted, warped and inferior infants." Was it any wonder, she asked, that "we as a race slide at an ever increasing speed towards the utter deterioration of our stock?"[22] Eager for the approval and support of the powerful and influential, Stopes sent Frances Stevenson, the Prime Minister's secretary, a copy of *Radiant Motherhood,* drawing special attention to the ideas in the chapter on eugenics, with which she believed David Lloyd George privately sympathised. After warning of the tens of thousands of "stunted, warped and inferior infants, who would invariably drain the resources of those with a sense of responsibility," she was certain her books could "do an immense deal to help him to get this country fit for heroes to live in, and bring along the crop of actual heroes too."[23]

This mixture of elitism, idealism and mainline class eugenics permeated much of Stopes' thinking. She shared Galton's belief that it was possible through positive, selective breeding to raise the qualitative level of future generations. But despite her impressive knowledge of paleobotanical fossils, she seemed to have very little interest in or understanding of either biometrics or Mendelian genetics, the two hereditarian explanatory models vying for the scientific soul of the eugenics movement in the opening decades of the century. Yet she never questioned the orthodox eugenic beliefs of the time that classes were the way they were primarily because of evolutionary, biological factors.

Like most orthodox eugenicists, (including the long-time president of the Eugenics Society, Major Leonard Darwin, the great naturalist's fourth son,) she worried that modern civilisation increasingly interfered with the workings of natural selection, preserving the unfit and discouraging the fit. While she certainly promoted positive eugenic policies encouraging the most highly evolved men and women to increase the number of their progeny, she was also one of a growing number of eugenicists who vigorously advocated new policies of negative eugenics based upon sterilisation, and, far more important, birth control. In becoming a life fellow of the Eugenics Society in 1921, she had visions of transforming it into "the biggest and most successful Society in England today" if only the membership would follow her lead in making constructive birth control - the blending of positive and negative eugenics - the instrument of racial reconstruction and progress.[24] It was the first of many such invitations from Stopes that the Society declined even while endorsing many of her arguments and adopting birth control as its principal eugenic weapon in the 1920s and 1930s.

Initially the main reason for keeping Stopes at arms length had much to do with the serious concerns of Leonard Darwin and other first generation eugenicists, including Galton himself, that birth control was already leading to smaller families among the educated and most successful sectors of society. These were people who presumably were endowed with the required personal qualities of foresight, discipline and self-control that contraceptive strategies required and that the labouring poor did not possess. In other words, birth control was already dysgenic, as the class characteristics of the plummeting birth-rate indicated. Its continued adoption was likely to exacerbate differential fertility and compound the dangers of race suicide. Despite mounting pressure within the Society to recognise that "all realistic eugenic proposals come down to birth control in this country," Major Darwin continued to find it a "delicate and difficult issue," and expressed the fear that "birth limitation will not be adopted voluntarily by the inferior types, and that there is considerable danger of its remaining a dysgenic influence."[25]

A second and in the end more compelling reason why the Society "cold-shouldered" Stopes, as she complained, was the difficulty of working with so quarrelsome a person, the dangers of being drawn into her constant battles with others in the birth control movement and the Catholic Church, her contempt for the medical profession, several of whose ornaments adorned the council of the Eugenics Society, and her increasing resistance to scientific research and progress.[26] By the middle of the decade, the Eugenics Society had begun to participate in the study of contraceptive practices "to ascertain to how poor and incompetent a section of the community it may be hoped that Birth Control would penetrate . . ."[27] Influenced by a new generation of younger, more scientific, reform-minded members like Julian Huxley and the psychiatrist C. P. Blacker, the Society, despite Darwin's doubts, agreed in 1926 to endorse birth control as a eugenic agent.[28] Nevertheless when the idea of closer co-operation with Stopes was broached, the usually compliant Darwin dug in his heels, complaining that Stopes "is an unscrupulous woman" whom he, and many other members disliked and distrusted. She was not only rude at Society meetings, but continually tried to drag the organisation into her fights with everyone in the birth control movement.[29]

Though Darwin was increasingly out of touch with the more birth control centred, research-oriented direction that the Eugenics Society took in the 1930s under the direction of its new general secretary Blacker, his assessment of Stopes and the need to keep her at a distance was widely shared within the eugenics camp where she was considered "quite impervious to reason." Huxley, for example, found her "rather terrible" and avoided ever going to any of her meetings, while Blacker found countless excuses to decline her invitations to lunch, dinner or weekends at her Surrey estate, Norbury Park.[30]

Throughout her life Stopes continued to claim that had the Eugenics Society welcomed her leadership when she offered it after the war, its history and hers would have been very different. For one thing she would not have been forced to establish her own eugenic and birth control organisation, the Society for Constructive Birth Control and Racial Progress "at such enormous personal cost of time, money and the many sacrifices involved in pioneering." One of her champions, the anthropologist George Pitt-Rivers recalled in a 1930s "Memorandum" (which Stopes had obviously approved, if not actually written), that had the Eugenics Society "not been false to the spirit of the tradition of leadership of its founder" [Galton] and permitted her to lecture to the membership, it might have accomplished all that she had done. But when the question of a Eugenic Society policy on birth control was discussed in a 1921 meeting, the memorandum continued, the participants concluded that there was little interest in birth control, and the working class would never adopt it. Stopes, according to Pitt-Rivers' account, pronounced the conclusions "preposterous" and to prove her point, vowed to take the Queen's Hall for a public meeting on birth control and pack its

2,000 seats. This she did on 31 May, and, Pitt-Rivers added, the Eugenics Society never forgave her. Despite her considerable achievements in subsequent years and indisputable eugenic qualifications, the Society never invited her to lecture. Marie Stopes' name, for example, does not appear among the roster of Galton lecturers. Having rejected the flamboyant prophet's vision and spurned her overtures, the Society, as one lined out paragraph of the Memorandum complains, then tried to "crab" Stopes' work and discredit her and the SCBC that had been established in the aftermath of the Queen's Hall meeting.[31]

Pitt-Rivers' Stopes-induced recollection of the origins of the Queen's Hall meeting as a bold response to a Eugenics Society snub, was one scenario. Another, told to her compliant biographer Keith Briant, was that she organised the meeting at the suggestion of the sympathetic David Lloyd George who, while declining to become a patron of her new clinic, suggested that she might hold "a great public meeting . . . to make birth control respectable."[32] The willingness of the Prime Minister's secretary, Frances Stevenson, to sit on the platform with a number of other prominent people in literature, politics, the trade unions, music, science and medicine, gives strong credence to Stopes' claim. It is evident, however, that she and her husband were already contemplating a large public event to launch a campaign to disassociate birth control from its negative, somewhat prurient connotations, and replace it with a "constructive" policy that would focus upon all aspects of married life, including the reproduction of fit, "healthy, happy, desired babies," as well as the "repression of lives which ought not to be started."[33]

Many of the speeches at the Queen's Hall Meeting were, with Stopes' encouragement, stridently eugenic in tone and content. She urged one medical officer to describe what it was like to have "to deal with the ruck, wastrels and throw-outs resulting from reckless breeding . . .," while others deplored the continued proliferation of the C3 population since the war, and called for a selective birth rate that could alone raise up the A1 population needed to elevate the race.[34] Stopes, who by her own account, was the hit of the evening, described constructive birth control as "the key to all racial progress," and promised that if "love and knowledge" became the ingredients of selective conception, we would see an "entirely new type of human creature, stepping into a future so beautiful, so full of the real joy of self-expression and understanding that we here today may look upon our grandchildren and think almost that the gods have descended to walk upon the earth."[35]

When, a few weeks after the Queen's Hall event, Stopes and her husband formed the Society for Constructive Birth Control and Racial Progress, they described as one of the "bedrock" tenets of the organisation the belief "that the haphazard production of children by ignorant, coerced, or diseased mothers is profoundly detrimental to the race." Another was the conviction that "many men and women . . . should be prevented from procreating children at all, because of their individual ill-health, or the diseased and degenerate nature of the offspring that they may be expected to produce." At the same time the SCBC regretted "the relatively small families of those best fitted to care for children." In accordance with its motto, "Babies in the right place," it was as much an aim of the SCBC "to secure conception" to those couples, as it was "to furnish security from conception to those who are racially diseased, already overburdened with children, or in any specific way unfitted for parenthood."[36]

Despite the strong eugenical foundations of Stopes' birth control crusade, there is a danger, as Deborah Cohen has pointed out, of confusing such overheated rhetoric with clinical practice. In examining the actual working of the Mother's

Clinic, it is evident that Stopes subordinated eugenic and
political considerations to a broader concern with helping the
mostly poor, often desperate women who visited the facility.[37]
While her writings about the poor were often harsh,
condescending, and censorious, and at times she seemed to
have difficulty thinking of them as being motivated by much
more than dangerous and ignorant impulses for immediate
gratification, Stopes could be deeply moved and horrified by
the individual plight of some of the impoverished mothers who
wrote her or came to the clinic. Her staff of midwives and,
when necessary, female doctors, who staffed the clinic tried, at
Stopes' direction, to create a simple, homey, comfortable
sanctuary where patients were to be treated with gentleness
and kindness.   Faced with staff who complained periodically
about the ingratitude and unwillingness of some of the poor
women who attended the clinic to pay a small charge, Stopes
nevertheless insisted that patients who could not or would not
pay were not to be turned away.[38] She spent a good deal of her
own and her husband's fortune in financing the clinic's
operations, and rarely ceased complaining about it.

However, it is less clear whether, as Dr. Cohen argues, "the
primary function of the Mother's Clinic was not to engineer a
eugenically fit Britain, but rather to teach women how to use
birth control so they could change their own lives."[39]   I would
suggest that while the two considerations were not joined at
the hip in the day-to-day operations of the clinic, birth control
was without question the most important enabling agent of
Stopes' eugenic goals.

She made this point repeatedly to Blacker, who, though
offended by her "flowry and highly-coloured books," had first
consulted her about contraceptives in 1924 when a medical
student at Guy's Hospital. He was fairly unique in his ability as
general secretary of the Eugenics Society from 1931 to 1952 to

maintain a cautious if distant, long term relationship with her despite periodic provocation. Shortly after he took over as general secretary, she forwarded to him a letter from a woman asking about condoms - which Stopes loathed for depriving women of the nutritional advantages of semen - with the note, "You are the man who has been advising condoms as distinct from proper clinical advice . . . so you deal with this." Blacker sent a sharp reply: "I do not deal with such cases. I return the letter."[40]

Blacker tried nevertheless to keep her informed about the Society's expanding role in the birth control movement and its support of the Oxford zoologist John Baker's search for the 'perfect' eugenic contraceptive, Volpar. His efforts were usually met with complaints about how she was not being given credit for all the great things she had done, accusations of "trying to wobble up my special field" and denunciations of laboratory and animal research into sexual physiology and contraception. Her clinic records, she insisted, provided all the research on the effectiveness and reliability of contraceptives that was needed.[41]

Unfortunately, Stopes was not always co-operative in providing her records, especially when she felt slighted by physician-run panels that excluded her from their deliberations because she lacked a medical degree. As the author of one of the most authoritative books on the subject, *Contraception,* and the recipient of thousands of letters of inquiry from unenlightened physicians, among others, she felt justified in boasting "I teach doctors."[42] When in 1925 the Mother's Clinic moved from Holloway Road to its current premises in Whitfield Street, Stopes began providing demonstrations on fitting birth control appliances for medical students and doctors as well as nurses, and in the early 1930s started holding "Doctors Days" while only relenting moderately in her less than flattering assessment of their intelligence, courage, knowledge, and usefulness.

But Stopes' efforts to sustain her pre-eminence and establish her scientific credibility in the field of birth control were increasingly compromised in the 1930s. by her exaggerated claims of success, rejection of improvements in contraception and refusal to co-operate with others. Despite her husband's hesitant warnings that she needed to be careful not to inflate the number of patients who visited the clinic and overstate her successes, Stopes' claims of failure rates of somewhere between 0.52 and 2.5 percent in anywhere from 5,000 to 10,000 cases was met with great scepticism, particularly when it was learned that she counted as a success any woman who did not return to the clinic or did not complain.[43]

Most other clinics that tried to follow their patients reported failure rates as high as 50 percent, in large part because women soon abandoned the reliable, if cumbersome Mensinga diaphragm and lactic acid jelly regimen prescribed, and reverted to less dependable methods, particularly coitus interruptus. When Lella Secor Florence sceptically contrasted the discouraging experience of the Cambridge Clinic and others with Stopes' dubious returns, Stopes went to Cambridge, organised a meeting, and attacked Florence and the other clinics as "amateur incompetents" who should be prescribing her own personally designed "Pro-Race cap."[44]

The more that medical research groups like the Birth Control Investigation Committee, working in conjunction with the expanding network of clinics, learned about the unreliability and ineffectiveness of many contraceptives the greater the concerns expressed about Stopes' extravagant claims. By the late 1920s virtually all of the clinics in Europe and the United States had spurned her Pro-Race device in favour of the Mensinga diaphragm which was much easier to fit and far more reliable.[45] When, as part of his search for a simple, reliable, inexpensive, eugenic contraceptive that could be used without medical intervention by "the stupidest and therefore the most undesirable members of society," John Baker questioned the spermicidal qualities of quinine, which Stopes prescribed as one of her "racial solubles", she ridiculed the reliability of laboratory experiments and denounced Baker for being tainted by commercialism, and for his lack of familiarity "with the habits of true scientific workers."[46]

Given her own habit of trying new contraceptives out not on guinea pigs but on herself and some of her married staff, sometimes with disgusting results, it is perhaps not surprising that she advised readers of the *British Medical Journal* and the *Lancet* in 1938, "Never put in the vagina what you would not put in your own mouth."[47] Though she finally relented and in 1939 began dispensing her own brand of condoms for "temporary protection", she always refused to prescribe Baker's Volpar, which upon its appearance in 1938 was quickly adopted by the Eugenics Society, most clinics affiliated with the National Birth Control Association, and soon after, by the Family Planning Association, as the most effective spermicidal gel on the market.[48]

By the outbreak of World War II, Stopes had become something of an anachronistic curiosity in the birth control and eugenics movements. So fearsome was her reputation for provoking disruptive quarrels that when the forerunner of the NBCA and FPA, the National Birth Control Council was established in 1930 , Stopes, despite her prominence, and her having actually proposed the resolution that brought the Council into being, had been invited to affiliate only at the insistence of an old friend, Helena Wright, who promised to undertake the thankless task of trying "to manage Marie."[49] Within three years Stopes resigned, complaining that although she was "personally . . . the pioneer of the birth control movement" who had founded the first clinic, delivered the first medical lectures on contraception, and persuaded the Ministry of Health in 1930 to permit local governments to provide birth control information in public health centres, the NBCA ignored her contraceptive recommendations, appointed to its executive committee people whom she distrusted, and declined to give her adequate credit for all she had accomplished. In a series of angry letters written during the remainder of the decade to officials of the BMA and the medical press, she charged that "after we had borne the brunt of all the pioneer work and at the moment it was ripe for development . . . [the NBCA] interfered with and undercut our work" by promoting unsafe contraceptives for commercial reasons.[50]

Although Stopes remained convinced that she alone had been responsible for the Ministry of Health's cautious decision in 1930 to permit local maternity and child welfare authorities to dispense birth control advice, she was in fact a very voluble part of a much broader campaign launched in 1922 by the first federation of voluntary clinics, the Society for the Provision of Birth Control Clinics, the Worker's Birth Control Group, the National Union of Societies for Equal Citizenship, several local Labour governments and the Eugenics Society. Stopes did unquestionably play a major role in first publicising in her *Birth Control News* the Ministry's quasi-secret enabling Memorandum (153/M.C.W.) which was likened by some enthusiasts to the Magna Carta.[51]

As far as Stopes was concerned, the major battle had been won in 1930. The government, spurred by her pioneering activities and demonstrations of what a model clinic might accomplish for the health and welfare of the poor, had taken the first step towards creating a national system of birth control facilities. Although she opened four more clinics in the 1930s in Aberdeen, Belfast, Cardiff and Leeds, she argued that additional voluntary facilities and organisations such as the NBCA, renamed the Family Planning Association in 1939, were unnecessary now that local authorities were free to establish their own. By the end of the decade fewer than twenty percent had done so, but the groundwork had been laid for rapid expansion after the war.

If one of Stopes' goals was then well on the way to being achieved, another, the qualitative improvement of the nation's stock, was more problematic. In many ways as her participation in the birth control movement began to wane and she focused increasingly on developing her questionable literary talents, her eugenic anxieties and resentment at being marginalised by the Eugenics Society increased. She not only opposed the Society's support of contraceptive research, but its financial backing of the NBCA, with which Blacker contemplated merging in 1938, and the struggling FPA, which for a period of time during the war the Eugenics Society housed rent free in its offices.[52]

To Stopes, all of this was a breach of trust and a diversion from the promotion of true eugenic advancement. She complained to the President of the Eugenics Society, Lord Horder, that Blacker was trying to deprive her of credit for creating and sustaining the birth control movement, and strongly resented his excluding her from meetings reserved for doctors.[53] Equally infuriating was the failure of the Eugenics Society to consult her when in the early 1930s, amidst a growing panic about an alleged decline in intelligence and increase in mental deficiency, it began promoting legislation to permit the voluntary sterilisation of the minority of mental incompetents whose fertility could not be contained by birth control. For one thing, Stopes believed in compulsory, not voluntary sterilisation, which she contended she had been quietly working for since 1921.   By "butting in" with its

disastrous, ill-conceived tactics to get a parliamentary measure
legalising useless voluntary sterilisation, the Eugenics Society
had frightened sentimental Labour politicians, reactionary
Catholics, and timid doctors, who were always ready to bolt.
What was needed, she insisted, was a campaign for
"compulsory sterilisation of those whose uncontrolled breeding
threatens the community."[54]

Stopes had never been reluctant to deliver eugenic
admonitions to any incautious degenerate who crossed her
path. These ranged from the parents of deaf and dumb children
to her own daughter-in-law. Convinced that it was "a crime
against his Country" that would make a mockery of her life's
work for "Eugenic breeding and the race," she refused to attend
her only son's wedding in 1948 and disinherited him for
contaminating his "splendid inheritance" by marrying a woman
with "an inherited physical defect" - poor eyesight - whose
offspring would in all likelihood bear the dysgenic stigmata of
spectacles.[55]

Stopes' exit from the centre of the birth control stage
accelerated during and after the war. The Whitfield Street clinic
was badly damaged during the blitz, and despite her
admonition to her nurses to continue fitting contraceptives until
the sound of gunfire and falling bombs made it too dangerous
to continue, she did close down temporarily and move the
operation to Bournemouth. If she needed further convincing
that the Nazis had specifically targeted her, she received it
when jettisoned bombs from German aircraft fell on her
eighteenth-century house and gardens in the Surrey hills.[56]

In the thirteen years remaining to her after the war, Stopes
remained vigorous and active, though something of a curious
relic from the past. Her works were no longer in the least
shocking to a new generation that even her captivated and
intimate young biographer Keith Briant admitted was surprised

to learn that she was still alive. Her long-time rival Margaret Sanger, by contrast was more active and famous than ever, playing a central role, along with Blacker, in the international birth control movement, an arena that Stopes never really entered. While Stopes continued to prescribe her old Pro-Race cap, Sanger was raising funds in support of Gregory Pincus' research into the development of the oral contraceptive pill, which enabled a far greater degree and range of sexual liberation than Stopes ever imagined, or, perhaps, would have approved.

Though in some ways Stopes was even more stridently eugenic in her views after the war, the Nazis, as Blacker had warned in the 1930s, had made the advocacy of eugenic policies in the post-war world politically impossible, while rapid developments in genetics required a serious rethinking of the scientific foundations of hereditarian causation. Stopes had never really paid much attention to those foundations, and while the old Eugenics Society continue to transform itself into a research unit for biosocial science and population genetics, she continued to rail against hypodermic injections, laboratory research, and the Ministry of Health for bullying doctors to give the new polio shots.[57]

Her ties to eugenics after the war were primarily through Blacker with whom she began to communicate again in 1951 following a long break. Though he resigned as general secretary the next year to work for the Simon Population Trust and to help Sanger establish the International Planned Parenthood Federation, Stopes, worried about her legacy, sought his endorsement for her claim to having founded the first birth control clinic, not only in Britain but in the world. By carefully defining the meaning of clinic to conform closely to her own - open every week day, having a broad medical purpose with qualified doctor or nurse in attendance, keeping case notes and records, publishing reports and under the control of known, responsible people - she insured that neither the Dutch nor the Americans could qualify for the honour.[58]

As far as she was concerned, the clinic that Dr. Aletta Jacobs had opened in Holland in 1882 and Margaret Sanger's short-lived effort in Brooklyn in 1917, which was quickly closed down by the police, lacked enough of these critical requirements to justify the claim she so desperately tried to reserve for herself. In the case of Sanger's clinic, Stopes implied in a later edition of *Contraception* that no patients had actually been provided contraceptive advice, to which the American countered in a 1931 letter to the sociologist and historian of contraception Norman Himes, that in fact 488 women had received such advice in the ten days that the facility was open. She went on to add, "the Clinic was organised on the lines of those I had visited in Holland and with glowing enthusiasm, I told . . . [Stopes] all about them in London in 1915." Sanger conceded that the word "Clinic" may be debatable, but those she saw in Holland "were just as properly and adequately managed as Dr. Stopes' Clinic which was run by midwives (not Doctors)," unlike those in America and the Netherlands.[59] The requirement of medical supervision as an essential definition of a clinic was guaranteed to provoke Stopes and did so until the end of her life.

Although Blacker long regretted that Stopes' influence and authority was initially derived from the timidity, confusion and resistance of his own medical profession he had no doubt that, however clinics were defined, she deserved the recognition she craved. He always admired her unstoppable determination and vision and in retrospect at least, was often amused, rather than offended, by her insatiable love of publicity and shameless proficiency at self-aggrandisement which had quickly made her in the 1920s the best-known advocate of birth control in Great

Britain. She would have said the world. In the obituary he wrote for the *Eugenics Review* in 1958, and in an *Encyclopedia Britannica* article in the 1960s, Blacker recalled her as an "evangelical visionary" - a pioneer and a prophet who possibly "transformed the sex habits of her generation," and who may someday be considered "one of the most remarkable women produced by this country in the twentieth century." But she was not always the easiest of people to get along with, Blacker confessed, and he counted himself "among the many who have regretted her inability to co-operate on equal terms with others who shared her aims and ideals."[60]

While Stopes certainly would have agreed with Blacker's assessment of her importance and conjecture about her likely standing in history, she had a very different assessment of her personality that she first expressed with her usual forthrightness in her new journal, the *Birth Control News* in 1922, and saw no reason to question throughout the remainder of her career. Describing herself in the third person as, "Impregnably honest, utterly fearless, incorruptible by the worldly lures which tend to weaken and deflect most reformers, yet sane, scientific and happy . . . Dr. Stopes, hating all conflict, is fighting on behalf of others."[61] Though some of her self-analysis may be seen as gratuitous self-deception, some of it was also quite accurate. Blacker, for example, would have mostly concurred, though I suspect his definition of sanity might have differed somewhat, and happiness, as her biographers suggest, was at best an illusive experience.

But Blacker also recognised that Marie Stopes was by any standard larger than life, and that her accomplishments in the advancement of birth control and sex education transcended the often infuriating defects of her dominating, self-righteous, litigious personality. It is impossible to read her vast, endlessly revealing correspondence without being fascinated, horrified, embarrassed,   infuriated,   entertained   and,   ultimately, profoundly impressed. If birth control did not always lead to the enduring passion, radiant married love and eugenic motherhood she so vividly envisioned for herself and others, her legacy is evident in the integration into the National Health Service in the 1970s of the voluntary clinic system that she launched, and in the much greater sexual openness, freedom and candour that for better or for worse - Stopes, given her Presbyterian and Quaker roots might have said worse - is one of the striking characteristics of modern culture.

If constructive birth control as an early effort at eugenic selection failed to provide the "new type of human creature", the god-like grandchildren whom Stopes once predicted would walk upon the earth - hers apparently warily because of their "goggles" - she nevertheless continued to try by leaving the Whitfield Street clinic and the Society for Constructive Birth Control, with their valuable freeholds, to the Eugenics Society. Unlike its benefactor who retained to the end her antipathy for the Family Planning Association, the Society welcomed close co-operation with the FPA and relied upon its much-needed assistance when it established the Marie Stopes Memorial Foundation as a charity to run the clinic. In leaving what she considered her most important legacy to the Eugenics Society, presumably because of her relationship with Blacker, Stopes was not only reaffirming her continued belief in the eugenic gospel, but also recreating the natural alliance for "race reconstruction" that she always claimed she wanted, but which had been rejected. When it came to birth control and eugenics, Marie Stopes was, if anything, persistent.

References:

[1]Stopes to Sanger 6 July 1915, Margaret Sanger Papers. Library of Congress

[2]Sanger to Norman Himes, 25 Sept. 1928, Norman Himes Archive, Box 45/F:515 The Francis Countway Library, Harvard University.

[3]Sanger to Stopes, 25 May 1920, Stopes Papers, British Library. Add. MSS. 58586 and Janet and C.F. Chance to Sanger, 19 July 1920, Sanger Ps., LC, Carton 21. Stopes to Sanger, 26 May 1920, Stopes Ps. Add. MSS. 58586.

[4]June Rose, *Marie Stopes and the Sexual Revolution*. London,

1992. p.144.

[5]Stopes to Sanger, 6 July 1915, Sanger Ps. LC Carton 21. , Marie Stopes, *Married Love: A New Contribution to the Solution of Sex Difficulties*. London, 1918.,Preface.

[6]Rose, *Marie Stopes*, pp.77-79.

[7]Stopes, *Married Love*, Chapter 10.

[8]Stopes, *Married Love*, Chapter 9.

[9]Marie Stopes, *Wise Parenthood: A Sequel to Married Love*. London, 1918, pp. 9-10, 17-25.

[10]Marie Stopes, *A Letter to Working Mothers on How to Have Healthy Children and Avoid Weakening Pregnancies*. Leatherhead, 1919, p.5-6, 13.

[11]Stopes, *Letter to Working Mothers*, p. 15.

[12]Marie Stopes, *Contraception (Birth Control): Its Theory, History and Practice. A Manual for the Legal and Medical Professions*. London, 1923, pp.382-83. See also, "The Tenets of the C.B.C.", 1923.

[13]For Stopes' strained relations with the medical profession see Richard A. Soloway, *Birth Control and the Population Question in England, 1877-1930*. Chapel Hill and London, 1982, Chapters 10, 12.

[14]Eugenics Education Society, Council Meetings Minute Book I, 26 July 1912, Eugenics Society Papers. Wellcome Institute for the History of Medicine.

[15]Aylmer Maude, *The Authorized Life of Marie C. Stopes*. London, 1924, p.29 and Keith Briant, *Passionate Paradox. The Life of Marie Stopes*. New York,1962, p.31.

[16]Archdall Reid to Stopes, 5 Nov. 1919, Stopes Ps. Add. MSS. 58565 and Stopes to Constance Brown, 18 October 1920, Add. MSS. 58644.

[17]Stopes, *Wise Parenthood*, p.7.

[18]Rose, *Marie Stopes*, p.96-97. For the Eugenics Society wartime policy see Richard A. Soloway, *Demography and Degeneration: Eugenics and the Declining Birthrate in Twentieth-Century Britain*. Chapel Hill and London, 1990), Chap. 7.

[19]Shaw to Stopes, 24 Sept. 1917, Stopes Ps. Add. MSS. 58493.

[20]National Birth-Rate Commission. *Problems of Population and Parenthood, Being the Second Report of and the Chief Evidence Taken by the National Birth-Rate Commission, 1918-1920*. New York, 1920, pp.252-53.

[21]*Queens Hall Meeting on Constructive Birth Control: Speeches and Impressions*. London, 1921.

[22]Marie Stopes, *Radiant Motherhood: A Book for Those Who Are Creating the Future*. London, 1920, pp.221-23; Marie Stopes, "Married Women: In the Future-Free," *The English Review*, 34, (May 1922), p.431.

[23]Rose, *Marie Stopes*, p.138.

[24]Stopes to Constance Green, 8 Dec. 1920, Stopes Ps., Add. MSS. 58644.

[25]*The New Generation: For Rational Birth Control*, I, No.6 June 1922, pp.4-5; *Eugenics Review*, 12, No. 1 (April 1920), pp. 71-73.

[26]Stopes to Cora Hodson, 24 March 1936, Stopes Ps., Add. MSS. 58645.

[27]Hodson to Stopes, 11 Dec 1923, Stopes Ps., Add. MSS. 58644.

[28]Darwin to Henry Twitchin, 30 January 1927, Eugenics Society Ps., Eug./C.87; *Eugenics Review*, 16, No. 1 (April, 1924), pp.101-04; No. 2 (July 1925), pp.141-43; 18, No. 2(July 1926), pp. 95-97; Eugenics Society, *An Outline of Practical Eugenic Policy*. London, 1926.

[29]Stopes to Hodson, 10 June 1927, ES Ps., EUG/K./1; Darwin to Hodson, 24 June.

[30]Lady Denman to Lord Horder, n.d., 1938, Eugenics Society Ps. Eug./C.172; Huxley to Blacker, 27 Feb. 1931, Eug./1/C.185

[31]George Pitt-Rivers, "Memorandum" (undated, probably 1936), Stopes Ps., Add. MSS. 58645.

[32]Briant, *Passionate Paradox*, p.143.

[33]Rose, *Marie Stopes*, p.147; See *Queen's Hall Meeting. . .Speeches*.

[34]Stopes to C. K. Millard, 10 May 1921, Stopes Ps. Add. MSS. 58564.

[35]*Queen's Hall Meeting. . .Speeches*.

[36]"The Tenets of the C.B.C.", 1923.

[37]Deborah Cohen, "Private Lives in Public Spaces: Marie Stopes, the Mother's Clinics and the Practice of Contraception", *History Workshop. A Journal of Socialist and Feminist Historians*, 35 (Spring, 1993), p.97.

[38]Cohen, "Private Lives," pp.106-08.

[39]Cohen, "Private Lives," pp.103.

[40]Blacker to Stopes, 10 Aug. 1924, Stopes Ps., Add. MSS. 58655; *Guy's Hospital Gazette*, 11 Oct. 1924, p.463; Stopes to Blacker, 11 Dec. 1933; Blacker to Stopes 15 Dec., Stopes Ps., Add. MSS. 58645.

[41]Stopes to Blacker, 17 February 1931; Blacker to Stopes, 18 February, Stopes Ps. Add. MSS. 58645

[42]Stopes to Hodson, 1 March 1926; Hodson to Stopes, 27 March; Stopes to Hodson, 29 March. Stopes Ps. Add. MSS. 58655.   For medical correspondence about *Contraception* see Add. MSS. 58569.

[43]Marie Stopes, *"The First Five Thousand," Being the First Report if the First Birth Control Clinic in the British Empire, "The Mothers' Clinic for Constructive Birth Control*. London, 1925; *Birth Control News*, April, 1930, p.189; June, 1930, p.22.

[44]Lella Secor Florence to Himes, 21 May 1930, Himes Archive/Box36/F:402; Lella Secor Florence, *Birth Control on Trial*. London, 1930.

[45]Florence, *Birth Control*, pp.35-36.

[46]Stops to Blacker, 17 Feb. 1931, Stopes Ps., Add. MSS. 58645.   Richard A. Soloway, 'The Perfect Contraceptive': Eugenics and Birth Control Research in Britain and America in the Interwar Years," *Journal of Contemporary History*. 30 (1995) p.639.

[47]See for example Stopes to Maude Kerslake, 14 Nov. 1924, Stopes Ps. Add. MSS. 58567 and *Lancet*, CCXXXIV, I, 5 March 1938, p. 577

[48]*Birth Control News*, XVII, 3 Feb. 1939, p.35. H. V. Roe to Blacker, 13 June 1944, Stopes Ps. Add. MSS. 58645.

[49]Blacker, "Obituary", *Eugenics Review*, L,   April 1958-January 1959, p.229; Rose, *Marie Stopes*, p.205.

[50]Stopes to NBCA, 17 Nov. 1933,; to the *Medical Times*, 29 February 1936, to the British Medical Asociation, 2 Feb. 1938, Stopes Ps. Add. MSS. 58643

[51] *Birth Control News*, Sept. 1930, p.72. See also Soloway, *Birth Control*, chap. 14.

[52] Soloway, *Demography and Degeneration*, pp. 203-15.

[53] Blacker to Maurice Newfield, 7 March 1932, Eugenics Society Ps., EUG./C.243.

[54] *New Generation*, XIV, 10 Oct. 1935, pp.119-20

[55] Ruth Hall, *Passionate Crusader: The Life of Marie Stopes*.

New York and London, 1977, pp.300-04; Rose, *Marie Stopes*, p.235.

[56] Rose, *Marie Stopes*, pp.223-24

[57] Stopes to Blacker, 20 March 1956, Stopes Ps. Add. MSS. 58645

[58] Stopes to Blacker, 20 Feb., 20 March, 1956; Blacker to Stopes, 16 March 1956, Stopes Ps. Add. MSS. 58645

[59] Sanger to Himes, 28 December 1931, Himes Archive, Box 45 F:/516

[60] *Eugenics Review*, L, April 1958-January 1959, pp.228-30.

[61] *Birth Control News*, July 1922, p.3

Marie Stopes and the Mothers' Clinics

Deborah Cohen

A few years before her death in 1958, Marie Stopes reviewed her enormous personal archive. Buried amidst exchanges with the century's literati, the country's best-known medical men, an assortment of guilt-ridden spinsters and impotent new husbands was a collection of letters to which Stopes attached particular importance. The documents in question issued from her five regional Mothers' Clinics: thick stacks of correspondence between Stopes and the midwives hired to spread her birth-control gospel. They were, on first inspection, rather unglamorous documents, especially when compared with the extraordinary secrets her other papers had to divulge. Most of the midwives simply wrote of the week's events, a few requested advice, a salary raise, or an extra package of the so-called "pro-race" caps the good doctor prescribed. Yet in Stopes' own estimation, the correspondence contained much of importance. No doubt recognising that the prosaic details of the clinics' daily travails would pale in comparison with her more notorious activities, she called attention to the papers' significance. Stopes wrote: "All should be kept for the future (British Museum?) as they each have a point of some historical significance and will interest posterity."[1]

An inveterate publicity hound, Marie Stopes would undoubtedly have been pleased that the Galton Institute has chosen to honour the seventy-fifth anniversary of her London Mothers' Clinic – the first birth control clinic in Great Britain. She might especially have welcomed the Institute's decision because Posterity has, on the whole, been less kind to her Mothers' Clinics than she had hoped. Although the British birth control movement has attracted many fine scholars, and Stopes herself the attentions of four biographers, her practical birth control work has largely been neglected, overshadowed by her remarkable career as a sex reformer and eugenicist. In Ruth Hall's thorough biography, for instance, the Mothers' Clinics to which Stopes devoted many years of her life receive only six pages, while her first love affair is granted twenty.[2] For more than three decades, the cache of Mothers' Clinics papers that Stopes sought so assiduously to preserve lay virtually untouched in the British Museum.

Yet to understand Marie Stopes, as well as the British birth control movement, we must examine her practical work in the Mothers' Clinics. Stopes' unapologetic eugenicism, self-promotion, and dogmatism have quite rightly made her an unsympathetic figure in many people's eyes. But if we look beyond what she said, and undoubtedly also believed, to what she actually did in her clinics, the picture becomes much more complex. I will demonstrate that in constructing a new model of medical intervention designed to enable women to control their own fertility, she placed her patients' health and happiness above all other - even eugenic - aims.

Re-assessment of Stopes' practical work calls into question the received wisdom about the British birth control movement. Historians of Britain have tended to interpret birth control as a repressive intervention, a mechanism of social control designed to curb the working-class birth rate. However, in dwelling on the eugenic attitudes manifest in the birth control movement's campaigns among the working classes, scholars have identified a critical *characteristic* of birth control propaganda as the most important *outcome* of its practice. They have made two errors. First, they have assumed that eugenic beliefs, and even eugenic rhetoric, necessarily translated into eugenic action. As we shall see, by no means were the policies and practices of the Mothers' Clinics consistent with Stopes' fervently-held and oft-expressed eugenic ideals. Second, historians have also disregarded the fact that working-class women came to the clinics because they wanted and sometimes desperately needed the services provided there. As a 21-year old mother of four told Mass Observation in 1945: "Oh there's enough babies in Poplar, if it's babies you want. We don't know how to stop 'em do we? I wish you'd tell us. We can't find out a thing in Poplar. I've heard of that woman, Marie Stopes is it? and I'm going to write to her. I've had my four a lot too quick and I want a rest from having babies."[3]

In 1921, Stopes and her husband, Humphrey Verdon Roe, opened the first English birth-control clinic in Holloway. By 1929, the London Mothers' Clinic had advised ten thousand patients.[4] During the 1930's Stopes established five regional clinics throughout the United Kingdom: Leeds and Aberdeen in 1934, Belfast in 1936, Cardiff the following year, and Swansea in 1943. In addition, the clinic maintained two Caravans, which travelled to small towns and rural areas in England and Wales. By 1945, approximately 43,000 women had visited the Mothers' Clinics for contraceptive advice.[5]

Today I will begin with an analysis of Stopes' intentions, as reflected in the Mothers' Clinics. I argue that Marie Stopes subordinated eugenic and political considerations to her overriding concern for the individual woman's health and happiness. I will then turn to the daily practice of the clinics. As I shall demonstrate, Stopes developed a new model of medical intervention – different from the dehumanising example of dispensaries and out-patients' departments – which enabled many of her patients to control their own fertility. At the Mothers' Clinics, women who had been forced to rely either on the 'self-control' of their husbands or on God's benevolence, learned how to regulate their own fertility. Yet the transition to 'female' methods of contraception was by no means simple. As we shall see, prejudices, misconceptions, and environmental obstacles conspired to make the practice of contraception a very difficult affair for many women.

Although the Mothers' Clinic was not the first birth-control clinic in the world, as Marie Stopes sometimes liked to claim, it was certainly the first in Great Britain. In the years following World War I, British birth controllers had trumpeted the virtues of what they termed 'practical work,' or the dissemination of contraceptive advice to the working classes. However, they had accomplished very little. Before Stopes founded the Mothers' Clinics, none of the oft-espoused objectives of the birth-control movement – the elimination of the "dysgenic populations," the improvement of women's health, the eradication of poverty – had been even partially realised. Though not necessarily the birth control movement's most likeable figure, Stopes was arguably its most important. Historians have agreed that Stopes' campaign for "constructive birth control" rescued contraception from the Neo-Malthusian backwater where it had foundered before the First World War. Rather than emphasising the perils of overpopulation as the Neo-Malthusians had done, Stopes justified birth control on medical and eugenic grounds, heralding contraception "as the keystone in the arch of progress towards racial health and happiness."[6] As historians have demonstrated, her theory of "constructive birth control" proved immensely persuasive in inter-war Britain, winning Stopes supporters even among those who had formerly eschewed the birth-control cause.

Not surprisingly, most historians have characterised Stopes' birth control work in terms of her eugenicism. Eugenics was far and away the most powerful weapon in Stopes' arsenal. Her promises to "quell the stream of depraved, hopeless, and wretched lives" fell on willing ears, for at the turn of the century, members of the "superior stock" had learned that they were reproducing only half as quickly as the "unfit."[7] Eugenics offered a solution to the "race suicide" being committed every day. One of the principal popularises of eugenic language, Stopes' personal commitment to eugenics is also well-established. A lifelong member of the Eugenics Society, she disinherited her son for marrying a woman "handicapped" by glasses.[8] Her public positions were often as extreme as her private fancies; in 1956, she claimed that one-third of the men in Britain should be sterilised, "starting with the ugly and unfit."[9]

That Stopes was a convinced eugenicist is beyond doubt. However, at issue here is not what she thought or said, but what she did in her birth control clinics. In the daily administration of the Mothers' Clinics, the two expressed concerns of her "constructive birth control" – the happiness of the individual woman and eugenics – often came into conflict. Should affluent women be given birth control advice? Were working-class women eligible for fertility counselling? To preserve the sanctity of the British race, eugenicists would have ignored the interests of the individual. In establishing the Mothers' Clinics' priorities, Marie Stopes decided differently.

Stopes first violated eugenic principles when she decided that all married women who asked for birth control at the Mothers' Clinics would be fitted, regardless of their wealth and social standing. According to Stopes, rich women needed birth control as much as poor women: "Her husband may be a millionaire, but I should still describe her as a poor woman if she did not know how to control her own motherhood and suffered from that want of knowledge."[10] Although she preached an ideal of four children per family, Stopes asserted that the clinics' criterion for treatment was whether the woman wanted more children. By making a woman's experience of marriage and motherhood her criterion, Stopes justified prescribing birth control in cases where eugenicists would have denounced her efforts as "dysgenic," or harmful to the race. Orthodox eugenicists had, after all, inveighed against the birth control movement because its results had proven "dysgenic." At the turn of the century, Karl Pearson had demonstrated that because affluent couples were practising contraception, "the less able, and the less energetic, are more fertile than the better stocks."[11] While Stopes' emphasis on the "positive racial" aspects of "constructive birth control" initially attracted eugenicists to her cause, her policies eventually proved antithetical to the Eugenic Society's most basic goals.

Not only did the Mothers' Clinics accept well-to-do patients, but Stopes actively sought out such women. Beginning in 1922, she sent midwives to the homes of women who wanted birth-control instruction. In a memo, Stopes detailed this service: "[T]he clinic has decided to initiate a service of highly trained Midwife-Nurses with SCBC training in addition who will visit ladies in their own homes, and there make the necessary examination and give advice on suitable contraceptives where the cases prove to be normal."[12] Although the vast majority of patients at the Mothers' Clinics were working- or lower-middle-class women, midwives did fit a number of middle- and upper-middle classes patients.[13] For example, one of the first patients at the Leeds Mothers' Clinic was the wife of an affluent optician.[14] Among the patients who received birth-control instruction at the London Mothers' Clinic on one day in August, 1938 were two schoolteachers' wives and a woman married to a film director.[15]

Even though the clinic's advice often prevented conceptions eugenicists would have encouraged, Stopes' slogan – "Babies in the Right Places" – continued to attract eugenically-minded followers. Especially persuasive for many people was her rhetoric about the dual function of "constructive birth control": preventing babies in the "C3," or poor and "degenerate," populations while assisting the "A1" couples to have the babies they desire and should have."[16] Stopes went to great lengths to stress the clinic's commitment to the "pro-baby" cases. The photographs of successful conceptions that adorned the Mothers' Clinics' walls attested to her sincerity. Stopes even claimed that the childless patients were "always nearest to my heart."[17]

Yet evidence from the Mothers' Clinics indicates that Stopes' decisions to give fertility advice to all women who were "childless and desire children and are themselves healthy," regardless of their economic status, sometimes enabled babies to be born in the "wrong" places.[18] In fact, one of the first fertility patients at the clinic was a tailoress from the East End of London who worked in a clothing factory for twenty-five shillings a week.[19] According to the eugenicists' criteria, many of the "pro-baby" cases advised at the Mothers' Clinics were "dysgenic" – some of them exceedingly so. In Cardiff, the white wife of a black man received "pro-baby" counselling.[20] The midwife at the Swansea Mothers' Clinic reported to Stopes about an obese patient with a harelip and a cleft palate – classic signs of racial "unfitness" according to eugenic criteria – who had recently become pregnant with the aid of the clinic.[21]

Stopes was a committed, but not a consistent eugenicist. Eugenics was not her only, nor necessarily her foremost, concern. In clinic policies, she rejected the most fundamental eugenic principles. When it came to crucial question of clinical practice, she clearly placed the individual woman's happiness over eugenic ideals. Inconsistent as it may seem, it was precisely this inconsistency that allowed the Mothers' Clinics to develop a model of instruction and intervention that gave priority to the individual patient's aims. For Stopes, the primary function of the Mothers' Clinics was not to engineer a eugenically fit Britain, but rather to teach women how to use birth control so they could change their own lives.

Of course, instructing women in birth control was no simple matter. On the day that the London Mothers' Clinic opened, a queue of women waited outside, attracted by posters announcing a free birth-control clinic in the Marlborough Road. Inside the clinic, Nurse Maud Hebbes prepared the examining room, while Mrs. Richardson, the receptionist tidied the waiting area, and Stopes conferred with Roe about the final details. At ten o'clock, Richardson unlocked the door, and waited for the first patients to appear. For several minutes, nothing happened; the women outside were too frightened to enter the clinic. Finally, Richardson went out and led each of them in by the hand.[22]

For the midwives at the Mothers' Clinics, this scenario was to become familiar. Midwives told stories of women too frightened to step inside the clinic, of women who peered into windows for months before entering, of women who passed through the waiting room but refused to be examined. Most working-class women attended dispensaries and out-patients' clinics only unwillingly; such visits always cost them precious time, usually subjected them to the scrutiny of medical staff, and sometimes led to a dreaded stay in hospital.[23] Many women were therefore hesitant to visit the Mothers' Clinic because they did not know what to expect. Rumours that patients were sterilised there discouraged many women from attending, as one midwife reported: "The patients are still slow in coming to Clinic and the most extraordinary ideas prevail about it ... A patient came yesterday from the largest housing estate in Cardiff and she said that when she told a few friends that she intended coming to find out what we did she was told 'They will take out your ovaries.'"[24]

Recognising that many women would feel uncomfortable in a birth control clinic, Stopes created very private sanctuaries to put her patients at their ease. The Mothers' Clinics were conscious and constructed spaces, monuments to her own theory of "constructive birth control." Furnished with a Jacobean table and plush armchairs, the reception room in her first clinic was designed to look like a comfortable sitting room, and painted blue with white trim. Framed pastel portraits of babies hung on the walls; a statue of a cherub perched on a pedestal in the corner. When in 1925 Stopes moved the Mothers' Clinic to a more spacious location in central London, she decorated the premises to similar effect. The ground-floor reception room was wallpapered in a blue-and-white willow pattern. Pictures of Stopes, her husband, and their child, Harry, hung on the walls, as did photographs of babies conceived after successful Mothers' Clinic fertility counselling. Upstairs, the two examining rooms were outfitted to resemble bedrooms, complete with marble fireplaces, delicately-patterned screens and fresh flowers in cut-glass vases.

Stopes recognised that the proper atmosphere depended as much on her staff as it did on the clinic's decoration. Early in her planning, she decided that midwives, not physicians, would dispense "constructive birth control." This "woman-to-woman" contact was the cornerstone of Stopes' philosophy. Every patient, she maintained, should feel "when she is at the clinic that there is a kind heart there to listen ... as well as to give her the more technical instruction in birth control."[25] At the Mothers' Clinics, each patient consulted only one person; the same nurse interviewed her, examined her, and taught her how to use the device. A stickler for professionalism, Stopes also placed great emphasis on the midwives' personalities, claiming that they had to be sympathetic, kind, and persistent not just to win their patients' trust, but even to get correct fittings. Most women, she wrote, would be nervous or frightened on their first visit to the clinic, and thus one of her aims was to put them at their ease: "Everything has been planned and thought out with the idea of making the clinic a *happy*, helpful place...where gentle and patient midwives and doctors, themselves married women, understand the problems and are ready quietly to spend all the time necessary to help and instruct inquirers."[26]

By employing married midwives – many who were of working-class origin – and by giving preference to older women who had children, Stopes sought to ensure that the nurses would understand their patients' concerns. "Cases needing surgical attention still continue to come in and one patient said, 'You don't know what a relief it is to be asked to sit down and given plenty of time to tell what is wrong.' She had put off getting medical attention because she didn't like to 'tell a man.'"[27] The midwives often expressed their empathy for patients by referring to their own experiences of motherhood and working-class life. Nurse Rae in Aberdeen, a mother of four, wrote to Stopes: "I'm out for cases, and not only cases but to tell everyone the good of your Birth Control – I had a hard life and I myself wish I had known of it."[28] According to the midwives, patients did feel more comfortable when they realised that they shared experiences with their nurses. Gertrude Thompson, a midwife at the London Clinic, reported: "I myself found I could not always get to [patients] until I mentioned I had little ones of my own."[29]

Although convincing women to be fitted was in many cases a significant accomplishment, the real challenge lay in teaching patients how to use their birth control appliances. A great many clinic patients either would not try to insert their appliances, or could not manage them. The cervical cap, which according to published reports was prescribed in nearly four-fifths of all clinic cases, requires a user who is both familiar with her anatomy and willing to touch herself, as the cap must be placed deep in the vagina. We must remember, however, that the vast majority of working-class women did not know about female barrier methods. In 1945, Mass Observation reported that the "complete ignorance of any measures which can be used by the woman" was "widespread."[30] Only sixty-two of the first 1,284 patients at the London Mothers' Clinic had previously used cervical caps.[31]

Many patients at the clinic were reluctant to use any "female" birth control device and variously condemned the idea as "unsanitary," "unhygienic," and "disgusting." When presented with a cervical cap, one patient at the Cardiff Clinic refused it, claiming that it was "disgusting," and said that she had "'got rid of things' regularly for years, much easier than bothering with caps, etc."[32] Even women who were willing to make the attempt found it difficult. Midwives often spent several hours trying to teach a patient one method, and frequently had to try several appliances. A woman who was not confident was often instructed to return a week later with the device inside her, so that the midwife could check its placement. If patients could not or refused to use barrier methods, the nurses supplied them with condoms, but usually urged them to return to be fitted.

Midwives found their patience often rewarded. Nurse Rae in Aberdeen recounted an emblematic story: "I had [Case 196] backwards and forwards to clinic time and again. I could not get her to feel confident in use. *Now she would not be without it.*"[33] More subtle, but nonetheless significant, was the way in which patients adopted the Clinic's language in describing birth control as a respectable subject. Mrs. Isabelle Wakeman wrote to Rae: "My chart will let you know how fear and hesitation had made me waste precious years of such a method...we will not keep quiet but will advise anyone seeking knowledge of such a clean and healthy method."[34] Another Aberdeen patient, Mrs. Huffer, claimed that "no mother should be without [contraception] because it is "most Hygienic."[35]

While Stopes could create an environment that attracted patients and midwives could spend hours instructing them, nothing the clinics did could ensure that women would be able to practice contraception once they returned home. To use birth control, a woman had to make decisive changes in an intimate and private area of her life. Those who were unable to practice birth control when they returned home cited a variety of reasons, including uncooperative husbands and their "uncertainty" or "lack of confidence" in the technique; many complained that the method was "too difficult" to use.[36]

Women brought up to believe that contraception was "unrespectable" or "immoral" had to overcome shame and embarrassment before they could practice birth control. Describing her own hesitations, a Women's Co-operative Guild member wrote: "I had a fight with my conscience before using a preventative."[37] One researcher found that a number of women loathed the entire notion of preparing for sex by inserting their diaphragms in advance.[38] Even as late as World War II, birth control was highly stigmatised in many working-class communities, and couples who had only one or two children were often ridiculed and harassed.[39]

In the cramped housing of working-class districts, it was often difficult to hide birth control use from family members and sometimes even from neighbours. The lessons women had learned behind a flower-printed Chinese screen in the tranquil and spacious Mothers' Clinic examining room were a completely different affair in their homes. For some working-class women, "home" consisted of two rooms, shared with as many as five children.[40] Only a minority of families had a bathroom.[41] Without a private bathroom or bedroom, and with few minutes in the day alone, women found it difficult to insert and remove their caps.

Thus it was often nearly impossible for a woman to practice birth control without her husband's knowledge. Few records indicate how men reacted to their wives' decisions to visit a birth-control clinic. Many husbands appear to have supported these choices, and in some cases, even to have encouraged them. In the late 1920's, the Liverpool Clinic determined that of 234 cases, husbands approved of the visits in sixty-six percent.[42] For whatever reasons, a number of men were eager that their wives be fitted – an enthusiasm that the women may not necessarily have welcomed. Nurse Rae in Aberdeen reported to Stopes about one woman whose husband gave her his paycheque in order that she could visit the clinic: "Her husband came home with his pay...He says: '*Here are my wages and off you got to 4 Gerrard St.;*'"[43]

Husbands' objections to certain methods, especially the condom, were registered by clinics and investigators. Nurse Underwood at the Leeds Clinic wrote to Stopes: "The majority of men object to the sheath method, I find."[44] Nurse Gordon at the Cardiff Clinic reported to Stopes about a patient whose husband refused to use a condom, ". . . saying he 'wouldn't be muzzled for anyone.'"[45] Another husband rejected condoms because he 'didn't like the look' of them"[46] Although many husbands who disliked abstinence or coitus interruptus (probably the two most prevalent methods of birth control among the working classes) might have welcomed "female methods," others could not be convinced. For some women, merely visiting the clinic was a subversive act.

Yet despite these obstacles, some women did succeed in practising contraception when they returned home.

Unfortunately, we know very little about how these women succeeded in negotiating obstacles that hampered others. Some women had the benefits of greater privacy, others returned to the clinic again and again until they were certain of the proper technique, a few gambled that their disapproving husband would not notice. Persistence, though no guarantee, may well have been decisive.

However, if the most pessimistic contemporary assessments are correct – and only fifty percent of the women who attended birth control clinics actually used their appliances, the results would still be significant.[47] These women had the means to reduce drastically their risk of unwanted, and often physically debilitating pregnancies. As their letters remind us, we should not underestimate what they had gained. As Mrs. March, an Aberdeen patient, wrote to Nurse Rae: "Words cannot express that feeling of security and safety that my husband and I now experience."[48] Another Aberdeen patient declared: "Result is perfect contentment of mind and enjoying good health, both physically and mentally. I cannot praise your Clino Cap highly enough. To me it has been a perfect friend in need."[49]

To conclude, the Mothers' Clinics offer a vantage-point onto a birth-control movement very different from the one historians have previously described. Without denying the significance of Stopes' beliefs or rhetoric, I have demonstrated that her practical work in the clinics was governed not by her loudly-proclaimed eugenic allegiances, but by her concern for the happiness and health of the individual woman. The point is not to vindicate Stopes' character, but rather, to assess how her decisions about clinical practice affected the women who were her clients. By directing attention to the practice of birth control, I have sought to take the working-class women who came to clinics seriously, to consider them not as pawns of the eugenics movement, but as people who wanted to change their lives.

The advice given at the Mothers' Clinics helped a great many women to solve the problems that had brought them there in the first place. Birth control was no panacea – it could not remedy problems caused by the structural inequalities of inter-war British society, nor could it radically transform marital relations within the home. Yet to those women who could use their Mothers' Clinics contraceptives, what they had gained was obvious. "I feel life is worth living now," wrote a patient at the London Mothers' Clinic to the midwife in charge, "so will you please give my best wishes to the Doctor, and please accept yourself the heartfelt gratitude of Mrs. Abelgate."[50]

Notes and References:

[1]This paper is based on an article first published in *History Workshop Journal.* "Private Lives in Public Spaces: Marie Stopes, the Mothers' Clinics, and the Practice of Contraception," *History Workshop Journal*, 35 (1993), pp. 95-116.

The names of patients at the Mothers' Clinics have been changed, to protect privacy. All references that begin Add Mss. refer to the Marie Stopes Collection at the British Library; all that begin PP/MCS refer to the Marie Stopes Papers at the Contemporary Medical Archive Centre of the Wellcome Institute for the History of Medicine.

Marie Stopes, 1950, Add Mss. 58614, British Library.

[2]Ruth Hall, *Passionate Crusader: The Life of Marie Stopes* (London, 1977).

[3]Mass Observation, *Britain and Her Birth-Rate* (London, 1945).

[4]Marie Stopes, *Preliminary Notes on Various Technical Aspects of the Control of Conception* (London, 1930).

[5]No comprehensive report of the Mothers' Clinics' attendances was ever assembled. I have arrived at this figure by collecting individual clinics' yearly reports. See Add. Mss. 58633, 58619, 58615, 58626, 58631, and PP/MCS, c. 21, Wellcome Institute.

[6]Marie Stopes, *The First Five Thousand* (London, 1925), p. 4.

[7]Marie Stopes, *Radiant Motherhood* (London, 1920), p. 221; See also Richard Soloway, *Birth Control and the Population Question in England, 1877-1930* (Chapel Hill, 1982), pp. 25-48.

[8]Ruth Hall, *Passionate Crusader*, pp. 300-302.

[9]*The Daily Sketch*, 18 October 1958, SA/EUG, k. 21.

[10]Marie Stopes, "Ideals and Practice of Constructive Birth Control," Speech given by Stopes to the Cambridge Society, 29 April 1930, PP/MCS, d. 19.

[11]Quoted in Soloway, *Birth Control and the Population Question*, p. 27.

[12]Memo of the Society for Constructive Birth Control, 1922? [Marlborough Road location], PP/MCS, c. 4.

[13]For information on the social class of the patients at the interwar clinics, see Norman and Vera Himes, "Birth Control for the British Working Classes: A Study of the First Thousand Cases to Visit an English Birth Control Clinic," *Hospital Social Service* 19 (1929), pp. 578-617; Norman Himes, "British Birth Control Clinics: Some Results and Eugenic Aspects of their Work," *Eugenics Review*, Oct. 1928; Diana Gittins, *Fair Sex: Family Size and Structure* (London, 1982), p. 168; "Report on Aberdeen Clinic," 13 March 1935, Add Mss. 58603.

[14]Nurse Gertrude Underwood to Stopes, 4 May 1934, Add. Mss. 58629.

[15]Case sheets, 14 August 1936, PP/MCS, c. 3.

[16]Marie Stopes, Essex Hall Meeting, 19 October 1922, PP/MCS, c. 45.

[17]Marie Stopes to Mrs. Rowland Hill, 13 October 1936, Add Mss. 58619.

[18]Marie Stopes, *Contraception* (London, 1923), p. 388.

[19]Alan Parkes and Dee King, "The Mothers' Clinic," *Journal of Biosocial Science*, April, 1974, p. 174.

[20]Gordon to Stopes, 8 February 1938, Add Mss. 58625.

[21]Gordon to Stopes, 25 May 1945, Add Mss. 58633. As Nurse Gordon's letter reveals, she was herself aware of the eugenic agenda, as well as the way in which clinic policy had violated it. "Unfortunately it is not a case where one would have chosen it to happen. . .She is of course very excited and grateful."

[22]As recounted by Dr. Evelyn Fisher in Parkes and King, "The Mothers' Clinic," p. 169.

[23]See Labour Research Department, *Report on Hospitals and the Patient, National Conference of Labour Women* (London, 1931); Bella Aronovitch, *Give It Time* (London, 1974).

[24]Gordon to Stopes, 28 January 1938, Add Mss. 58625.

[25]Marie Stopes, Society for Constructive Birth Control Meeting, 22 November 1928, Add Mss. 58589.

[26]Stopes, *Birth Control To-day*, p. 179.

[27]Gordon to Stopes, 17 June 1938, Add Mss. 58625.

[28]Rae to Stopes, 4 April 1935, Add Mss. 58603.

[29]Nurse G. Thompson to Stopes, 10 August 1925, PP/MCS, c. 6.

[30]Mass Observation, *Britain and Her Birth-Rate*, p. 55.

[31]Stopes, *The First Five Thousand*, p. 42.

[32]Gordon to Stopes, 21 July 1939, Add Mss. 58625.

[33]Rae to Stopes, 15 June 1936, Add Mss. 58606.

[34]Mrs. Isabella Wakeman to Rae, n.d., attended clinic 22 October 1937, PP/MCS, c. 36.

[35]Mrs. Huffer to Rae, 9 March 1936, PP/MCS, c. 36.

[36]See Lella Secor Florence, *Birth Control on Trial* (London, 1930), p. 63, p. 73; Himes, p. 610.

[37]Quoted in Margaret Davies, ed., *Maternity: Letters from Working Women* (London, 1978 [1915]), p. 94.

[38]Florence, p. 68.

[39]Elizabeth Roberts, *A Woman's Place* (London, 1984), pp. 85-86.

[40]Spring-Rice, p. 129. On overcrowded housing, see also G.D.H. Cole and M.I. Cole, *The Condition of Britain* (London, 1937), pp. 156-166; D. Caradog Jones, *Social Survey of Merseyside*, vol. 1 (Liverpool, 1934), pp. 103-130, pp. 162-192; Allen Hutt, *Condition of the Working-Class in Britain* (New York, 1933), pp. 123-152; John Burnett, *A Social History of Housing, 1815-1985* (New York, 1986), pp. 219-249, pp. 331-333.

[41]E. Roberts, p. 132; Jones, pp. 115-116.

[42]Himes, p. 612.

[43]Rae to Stopes, 21 January 1935, Add Mss. 58602.

[44]Underwood to Stopes, 22 October 1937, Add Mss. 58630.

[45]Gordon to Stopes, 15 September 1939, Add Mss. 58625.

[46]Gordon to Stopes, 7 September 1945, Add Mss. 58633.

[47]Florence, p. 157.

[48]Mrs. J. March to Rae, 11 June 1937, PP/MCS, c. 36.

[49]Agnes Denton To Rae, 5 March 1937, PP/MCS, c. 36.

[50]Mrs Elizabeth Mary Abelgate to Nurse Thompson, 2 September 1924, PP/MCS, c. 12.

"Marie Stopes: Secret Life" – A Comment

John Timson

Every generation seems to produce critics determined to undermine the achievements of outstanding men and women of the past. Using 20:20 hindsight and a careful selection of the available material and, being convinced that their own set of social and cultural values is the test by which all actions at all times should be judged, these critics aim to devalue the work of those who have been prominent in almost every field of human endeavour. Today the most powerful weapon such critics have is probably the television documentary. Seen by millions who often have little or no other knowledge of the subject these documentaries can all too easily become the accepted version of events. This film is very far from being the worst example of such spin-doctoring of historical fact but neither is it entirely free from bias.

It is sadly true, and perhaps reflects badly on our education system that a person's sexual adventures excite more interest than what they have actually achieved in life. The film panders to this by spending a quite unnecessary amount of time on Marie Stopes' personal life while making little of her very successful career as a research scientist before she turned her attention to birth control. Perhaps the makers were hoping to suggest that they had discovered some remarkable, presumably new, sleazy aspects of her personal life. Many viewers may well have believed this but in fact, for those interested, Marie Stopes' recent biographers, Ruth Hall and June Rose, had

95

already recorded both her personal and professional life in great detail.

Much is made of Marie Stopes' interest in eugenics, described as a 'discredited' theory but never explained. The word itself is used as a term of abuse, as if anyone holding eugenic views is by definition at best wrong, probably bad, quite possibly evil. There is a quite confused section in the film where it is said that Marie Stopes tried to put her eugenic theories into practice by carefully controlling the environment in which her son was raised. Lamarck and Lysenko, who believed in the inheritance of acquired characters, would have seen this as possible. However, there is no scientific evidence to support their theories and a great deal to suggest they are false. It seems unlikely that Marie Stopes with her knowledge of biology would have believed she could change her son's genes in that way.

Marie Stopes' eugenic concerns were, I believe, to do with the different breeding rates of what she saw as desirable and undesirable sections of the population. It is suggested in the film that this was her motive for establishing her clinics - to cut down the number of children being born to undesirables. Perhaps she had this in mind, perhaps not, but as Deborah Cohen's paper in this volume shows Marie Stopes and her helpers were deeply concerned with the problems of the individual women who attended the Mothers' Clinics. Even as single-minded a person as Marie Stopes could have mixed motives for her actions and surely it is the results of these actions which are really important. Freeing women from the burden of repeated unwanted pregnancies must be one of the finest achievements of the 20th century and Marie Stopes is rightly regarded as having played a major role in bringing this about.

There is, of course, some good material in the film. In particular there are the interviews with Marie Stopes' son, daughter-in-law, publisher, and friend which it is useful to have on record and available for future historians. It is to be hoped that the unused footage has also been preserved. Whether the interviews with a disgruntled former employee are of any value at all is doubtful. The bitterness and envy which is so clearly apparent devalues her remarks which are mostly personal and do no more than show that not everyone liked Marie Stopes. In one sequence she says disparagingly that Marie Stopes regarded herself as beautiful. The photographs shown in the film of the young Marie Stopes as a student are of an attractive young lady and in those of her in later life she looks much younger than her age. Perhaps Marie Stopes was not entirely wrong?

A final thought. Marie Stopes was egoistic, domineering, and supremely self-confident, often convinced that she, and she alone, was right. She was also extremely hard-working and often demanded more of those around her than they were able, or prepared, to give. She needed to be all of these things, particularly as a woman at that time, to be able to achieve her goals yet these aspects of her character are criticised in the film. But if Marie Stopes had been just another average woman of her time would anyone have even considered her as a subject for a television documentary?

Marie Stopes International Today

Patricia Hindmarsh

When Marie Stopes established the first family planning clinic in London in 1921, she did so in response to the desperate struggle of women trying to cope with too many children and too many pregnancies, many of them unwanted. She wanted to enable women to enjoy 'voluntary motherhood' - in other words, to give them the means by which they could choose when to have - or not have - children.

75 years later, the work begun by Marie Stopes is being continued by Marie Stopes International, which provides reproductive health care and family planning services to women and their families in 26 countries around the world.

Today, we are much more than a simple provider of family planning. Through our advocacy programme, we are playing a central role in shaping international policies on population and reproductive health. We have launched new initiatives to meet the needs of refugees and other under-served groups, while through our subsidiary, Options, we offer a unique consultancy facility used by leading development agencies and governments around the world.

Our mission, however, remains unchanged. Following in Marie Stopes' footsteps, Marie Stopes International works to ensure children by choice, not chance.

Today, I am here to talk to you about the what, where, why and how of our work - to show you Marie Stopes International at the cutting edge of developments in the field of population and reproductive health.

MSI as we know it today was set up in 1976, by our Chief Executive Dr. Tim Black, who, as a medical practitioner, had had first hand experience of the very real problems faced by women without access to family planning services.

Working as a medical superintendent in New Guinea in the 1960s, Tim Black was visited one morning by a woman who had a baby with an umbilical hernia. He decided to operate, explaining in Pidgin that there was a chance that the baby might not survive. However the operation was successful, and he returned to the mother with the good news, only to see her look, surprisingly, disappointed. She explained that she had secretly wanted the baby to die, she had too many children, no husband, the coconuts were too few, and so on.

This case history illustrates a basic human need which is still as urgent today. Every year, world-wide, half a million women die from causes related to pregnancy or childbirth; 20 million unsafe abortions are carried out; and around one in every 16 children die before reaching their first birthday, due to causes related to poor birth spacing or the poor health of their mother. The majority of these cases occur in the developing world - the poorest countries on our planet, least able to afford this tragic waste of life and resources.

Yet the problem is no longer low awareness or lack of demand for family planning services. Around 120 million women around the world want to limit or space their families, but lack access to acceptable or affordable methods of contraception which would enable them to do this.

If we met the unsatisfied demand for family planning and reproductive health care, we could prevent unwanted and unplanned pregnancies, reduce infant and maternal mortality rates, improve the health of women and their families, and make a significant contribution to balancing the needs of growing populations and scarce natural resources.

This is the critical need which informs and guides the work of Marie Stopes International, which aims to meet the growing demand for family planning and reproductive health care with low-cost, accessible and quality services.

In the UK, Marie Stopes International operates six clinics in London, Leeds and Manchester, as well as a nation-wide network of local pregnancy advisory centres and vasectomy clinics. Our reproductive health services include family planning, well woman and well man checks, vasectomy and female sterilisation, and termination of pregnancy. We are the largest private sector provider of family planning services in Britain.

MSI's UK clinics are the backbone of an international network, providing both funding and a model of good service, based on the principles of quality of care and individual choice. Our first overseas programme was launched in India in 1978, followed quickly by programmes in Sri Lanka, and Kenya. In 1996, Marie Stopes International has reproductive health care programmes operating successfully in 26 countries across Asia, Africa, Latin America and Europe.

I should explain here, that we are not trying to create an empire of mini MSI's. We believe that services can only be delivered effectively through the active participation of local people. Marie Stopes International establishes local partner NGOs who are responsible for delivering and managing services, while we provide fund-raising support and technical assistance, liaise with international donors, and carry out project monitoring and evaluation. Together with our partner organisation in each country, we work closely with local communities, health professionals, the private sector, and government ministries.

Each country programme varies according to local conditions, but typically begins with establishing a clinic base in an urban centre, followed by satellite posts in outlying areas, and mobile outreach services to reach remote rural or marginalised urban communities.

MSI's work in Indonesia will give you an idea of how a country programme is developed.

Indonesia is the fourth most populous country in the world, with a predominantly rural, agrarian population. Figures suggest that the *majority* of women routinely resort to self-induced abortion as a method of family planning, reflecting a lack of access to family planning services particularly among rural and poor urban communities. Unsafe abortion on this scale is creating a serious public health problem, reflected in high levels of maternal mortality and morbidity.

MSI has been working in Indonesia since 1986 to help address some of these urgent needs. Our local partner Yayasan Marie Stopes Indonesia - YMSI - now operates three clinics on the island of Java, the most densely inhabited of Indonesia's islands, and home to 60 per cent of the country's population. All three of these clinics provide a full range of reproductive health care services, including family planning supplies and counselling, female and male sterilisation, mother and child health care, and obstetrics.

A mobile clinic provides services to rural and low-income urban areas, ensuring that quality services remain accessible to even the poorest families. Both clinic-based and mobile services are provided for a modest fee, or free-of-charge for those unable to pay.

YMSI have an extensive training and education programme which works with a variety of community groups. Their education team distributes informative, visually attractive leaflets on a variety of topics, runs demonstrations on family planning methods, and holds discussion groups. A number of participants in these programmes have become 'advocates' for family planning, acting as health promoters in their own neighbourhoods.

One of YMSI's particularly successful initiatives is a training programme for traditional birth attendants - TBAs, who play a very important role in delivering primary health care in rural communities, and as such, are highly respected and influential. Most TBAs do not have any formal education or training, and their standards of care are very variable. During YMSI's four-day programme, each TBA is taught how to diagnose pregnancy, check for signs of anaemia or other problems, and recognise symptoms of more complex cases which need referring to YMSI's clinics. They are taught how to wash and prepare for delivery, and supplied with a birthing kit which includes all the basic equipment they need.

YMSI's training programme is very popular and well-regarded: not only does it ensure that women receive good care during childbirth, but it is also helping to develop the skills of local women, and build good community relations.

YMSI enjoys an excellent relationship with the Government of Indonesia, who provide support for both clinic-based activities, and mobile services. Once a month, for example, the clinics hold a 'Safari Campaign Day' - Posuandu - financed by the government, which enables all services to be provided free-of-charge.

Our programme in Indonesia has been funded and supported by the Galton Institute and I would like to express the warmest thanks of MSI to the Institute for making this important work possible.

Our programmes in Indonesia, and elsewhere, are constantly changing and evolving in response to new concerns and priorities. In Sierra Leone, for example, the outbreak of a violent civil war in 1995 forced our partner MSSSL to shut down clinics operating in the north and east of the country. Many people left their homes, and fled to the capital city, Freetown, where they became IDPs - internally displaced people. MSSSL immediately launched an emergency programme to take services to people living in both informal and formal refugee camps around the city. They run a mobile clinic, from which a team of doctors and nurses provide family planning services, treatment and counselling for STDs, and an emergency referral service for women suffering complications in labour to MSSSL's obstetrics unit.

People are often surprised that refugees need family planning services. A common reaction is "surely women can't be thinking about sex at a time like this." MSI has been working with refugee communities since the 1980s, and our experience shows that refugee women have an absolutely critical need for reproductive health care.

Basic living conditions in refugee camps are often very poor, particularly in the early phases of establishing an emergency programme. For example, food rations can be erratic. And, with a shortage of clean water and sanitation facilities, many refugees commonly suffer from malnutrition, diarrhoea, scabies and other health problems. Few women want to bring a baby into the world in conditions like these. Yet, as a refugee, women are at greater risk of an unwanted pregnancy, contracting a sexually transmitted disease, or suffering from complications in labour due to poor health or lack of professional care. And, as we have seen in Bosnia and other war zones, refugee women have a greater risk of rape or sexual violence.

In these circumstances, I think there are few people who would not agree that refugee women should have the same rights to protect themselves against unwanted pregnancies and STDs, as any other woman.

MSI's Refugees Initiative is working to ensure that reproductive health care becomes an integral part of emergency aid to refugees and internally displaced people. We currently operate four emergency programmes, with a number of new programmes in the pipeline. Our Refugees Initiative is also carrying out a variety of advocacy, technical assistance, and fund-raising projects, to raise awareness of this critical issue, and catalyse action by the international community.

In tandem with our work on refugees, Marie Stopes International is looking at new ways of meeting the needs of other under-served groups, including adolescents and men. Although many societies - including our own - feel uncomfortable about acknowledging adolescent sexuality, teenage pregnancies and the increasing incidence of STDs among this age group, represent a major public health problem. Young women who become pregnant at an early age are more likely to die in childbirth or suffer complications in labour, and their children have increased risks of early mortality. Yet, there are very few services specifically for teenagers in traditional family planning provision. We are trying to remedy this. In Kenya, for example, MSI is running a project with the National Youth Service, which uses peer educators to raise awareness of STDs, and other sexual health issues, and promote condom use, and we have similar projects in Ethiopia, Romania and the Philippines.

Men have also been ignored by traditional family planning programmes, although as heads-of-household, they have a key role to play in encouraging the acceptance of family planning and other services in their community. Our experience shows that if you provide services for men, they will listen and respond. We have a number of male peer education schemes, such as the Man-to-Man project in Malawi which runs education activities in factories and workplaces. And, in a new initiative, we are opening male clinics which are designed to offer a sympathetic and friendly atmosphere for men. In the Philippines this year, we opened a night clinic in Metro Manila which offers an accessible location and convenient opening hours for taxi drivers, and other night workers. Services include the provision of contraceptive supplies and information, treatment of STDs, and Well Man check-ups.

So, in 1996, Marie Stopes International is working in 26 countries around the world, providing a steadily expanding range of services to meet a growing demand for reproductive health care. The big question, of course, is how do we pay for all this?

Income from the UK clinics helped to set up our overseas programmes in the early days, and it continues to support them. We also enjoy an excellent relationship with a variety of donors, ranging from development agencies such as the UK's Overseas Development Administration, to trusts, foundations, and private individuals. Their funding plays an important role in helping to pump-prime new clinics and new programmes.

However, the acid test we apply to all our programmes is sustainability. All too often, NGOs set up a clinic or health project in a community, only to see it closed down a few years later because their funding has run out. MSI's aim is to build enduring   programmes   of   reproductive   health   care   in partnership with local organisations, which can sustain themselves through user fees, donations, and local fund-raising.

Our programmes use a combination of cost recovery and cross-subsidy to fund their operations. Services are provided for a locally set fee, carefully targeted to ensure they remain accessible to low-income clients. Fees from clinics in middle class areas help to support a subsidised treatment fund which enables services to be provided free-of-charge to the poorest communities.

In Kenya, for example, MSI's clinics in the wealthier districts of Nairobi, help pay for the operating costs of clinics in the very poor slum neighbourhoods which are unlikely to ever generate enough income to support themselves. We call this 'Robin Hooding'.

These mechanisms work. In most developing countries, people are accustomed to paying something for their health care. A fee-paying service also acts as an assurance of quality, and ensures that the take-up of family planning and other services is based on individual choice rather than coercion. After all, people will not pay for a service they do not actually want. Our programmes in Ethiopia, India, Kenya, Madagascar, Romania and Sri Lanka have achieved financial sustainability. And 11 other country programmes are halfway to meeting this goal.

In this way, Marie Stopes International has developed a new model for delivering reproductive health care which can reach even the 'poorest of the poor'. As a social entrepreneur, we use modern business, financial and marketing techniques - but for a social end, rather than commercial gain.

Contraceptive social marketing - known as CSM - is a highly successful development of this philosophy. CSM programmes use commercial marketing techniques to promote and sell contraceptives such as the oral pill and the condom through garages, supermarkets, hairdressers, and other retail outlets. By taking contraceptives out of the medical arena, CSM addresses many of the crucial reasons which deter people from protecting themselves against unwanted pregnancies or sexually transmitted diseases. Family planning clinics, for example, are traditionally part of mother-and-child health care - not a very inviting environment for teenagers, single women or men. Since CSM programmes do not depend on a traditional health service infrastructure, they can increase the take-up of contraceptives very quickly and cost-effectively even in isolated rural areas.

Marie Stopes International is currently operating six CSM programmes, including a new programme in Uganda launched last year as an integral part of the Ministry of Health's strategy for tackling the spread of sexually transmitted infections. Uganda has been very badly hit by AIDS and HIV, which is now the leading cause of adult death in the country. The costs of trying to treat AIDS-related illnesses represent an enormous burden for this very poor country, which has a national health budget of just four dollars per head.

In a case like this, the old saying "prevention is better than cure" has never been truer. So far, our CSM programme in Uganda has developed a locally branded condom, called 'Lifeguard', which is being promoted on television, radio and other mass media as a means for individuals to protect themselves against sexually transmitted diseases. A sales team are visiting retailers to encourage them to stock the condom, and ensure they can explain to customers how to use it effectively. 'Lifeguard' is being treated exactly like any other commercial product - with the vital difference that it will help to save lives, prevent the spread of STDS, and prevent unwanted pregnancies.

CSM programmes offer some new lessons for delivering cost-effective, sustainable programmes of reproductive health care. MSI's subsidiary, Options, was established in 1992 to enable MSI's experience and expertise to be used by other organisations. While the US has a generous supply of policy-makers, academics and professionals working on reproductive health care, the UK has a skills shortage in this crucial area. Options helps to fill this gap. It provides a unique consultancy service on reproductive health care and family planning for governments, international agencies, and other clients, offering a wide range of services including technical assistance, and project management. Options has carried out assignments in over 30 countries, and is the ODA's designated Resource Centre for international work in reproductive health and family planning.

With initiatives such as social marketing, our commitment to sustainability, and cost-recovery, MSI's programmes do an excellent job of using scarce financial resources extremely effectively. At the same time, we believe it is crucial for the international community to maintain and strengthen their commitment to population and reproductive health.

The bill for providing reproductive health care and family planning to meet the unmet demand stands at $17 billion per year and is set to continue rising. Meanwhile, budgets for population assistance have steadily declined over the last decade. These sums simply do not add up.

It is absolutely vital that we reverse this trend, educate key international policy-makers, and mobilise new resources for family planning and reproductive health care.

MSI's advocacy programme works closely with parliamentarians, UN agencies, and other international bodies to raise the profile of reproductive health issues, and increase support for population and reproductive health programmes. We played an active role in the preparations and follow-up to the International Conference on Population and Development in Cairo in 1994, and the 4th UN Conference on Women in Beijing in 1995. In the European arena, MSI acts as the secretariat to the European Parliament Working Group on Population, Sustainable Development and Reproductive Health. We advise on key pieces of European Union legislation, provide speech notes and briefing papers for parliamentarians, and facilitate seminars, conferences and other events.

We are now exploring ways of sharing our experience in advocacy to help build a strong international voice for reproductive health care. In 1995, with support from UNFPA we published a 'Handbook to EU Funding for Population and Reproductive Health', followed this year, by a practical training workshop for European NGOs on 'Working with Parliamentarians and Government Officials'. Initiatives like these are helping to develop the advocacy skills of newly emergent reproductive health NGOs in Europe, and guide them through the complex political byways of the EU. This year we have begun providing technical assistance on advocacy to our overseas partners, and also launched a major training programme on advocacy for the 'Partners in Population and Development' - ten developing countries considered to have model population programmes.

Over the past 20 years, the work of Marie Stopes International has developed in response to the changing world around us. And, as a dynamic organisation, we will continue to evolve in order that we can meet the needs of new generations to come most effectively.

Already in this last decade, there has been a fundamental shift in attitudes towards family planning and reproductive health care. Firstly, the traditional idea of family planning as a tool for population control is no longer valid. While there is no doubt that growing populations remain a critical item on the global agenda, it is now recognised that traditional population programmes, with their emphasis on meeting demographic targets, have not been effective. Secondly, population is now seen as part of a complex equation with the environment, consumption, and poverty. If we are serious about tackling population pressures, we must also address the problems of sustainable development, and the status of women, for example.

Marie Stopes International is committed to addressing these challenges. Through our effective and innovative programmes of reproductive health care, we will continue to follow our mission of children by choice, not chance, and serve women and their families around the world.

Index

111